INDIANS

POCAHONTAS, *Seymour*
SACAGAWEA, *Seymour*
SITTING BULL, *Stevenson*
TECUMSEH, *Stevenson*

NAVAL HEROES

DAVID FARRAGUT, *Long*
GEORGE DEWEY, *Long*
JOHN PAUL JONES, *Snow*
MATTHEW CALBRAITH PERRY, *Scharbach*
OLIVER HAZARD PERRY, *Long*
RAPHAEL SEMMES, *Snow*
STEPHEN DECATUR, *Smith*

NOTED WIVES and MOTHERS

ABIGAIL ADAMS, *Wagoner*
DOLLY MADISON, *Monsell*
JESSIE FREMONT, *Wagoner*
MARTHA WASHINGTON, *Wagoner*
MARY TODD LINCOLN, *Wilkie*
NANCY HANKS, *Stevenson*
RACHEL JACKSON, *Govan*

SCIENTISTS and INVENTORS

ALECK BELL, *Widdemer*
ELI WHITNEY, *Snow*
GEORGE CARVER, *Stevenson*
GEORGE EASTMAN, *Henry*
HENRY FORD, *Aird-Ruddiman*
JOHN AUDUBON, *Mason*
LUTHER BURBANK, *Burt*
MARIA MITCHELL, *Melin*
ROBERT FULTON, *Henry*
SAMUEL MORSE, *Snow*
TOM EDISON, *Guthridge*
WALTER REED, *Higgins*
WILBUR AND ORVILLE WRIGHT, *Stevenson*
WILL AND CHARLIE MAYO, *Hammontree*

BOOKER T. WASHINGTON, *Stevenson*
CLARA BARTON, *Stevenson*
DAN BEARD, *Mason*
JANE ADDAMS, *Wagoner*
JULIA WARD HOWE, *Wagoner*
JULIETTE LOW, *Higgins*
LUCRETIA MOTT, *Burnett*
MOLLY PITCHER, *Stevenson*
SUSAN ANTHONY, *Monsell*

SOLDIERS

ANTHONY WAYNE, *Stevenson*
BEDFORD FORREST, *Parks*
DAN MORGAN, *Bryant*
ETHAN ALLAN, *Winders*
FRANCIS MARION, *Steele*
ISRAEL PUTNAM, *Stevenson*
JEB STUART, *Winders*
NATHANAEL GREENE, *Peckham*
ROBERT E. LEE, *Monsell*
TOM JACKSON, *Monsell*
U. S. GRANT, *Stevenson*
WILLIAM HENRY HARRISON, *Peckham*
ZACK TAYLOR, *Wilkie*

STATESMEN

ABE LINCOLN, *Stevenson*
ANDY JACKSON, *Stevenson*
DAN WEBSTER, *Smith*
FRANKLIN ROOSEVELT, *Weil*
HENRY CLAY, *Monsell*
JAMES MONROE, *Widdemer*
JOHN MARSHALL, *Monsell*
SAM HOUSTON, *Stevenson*
TEDDY ROOSEVELT, *Parks*
WOODROW WILSON, *Monsell*

Liliuokalani

Young Hawaiian Queen

Illustrated by Leslie Goldstein

Liliuokalani

Young Hawaiian Queen

by Shirlee Petkin Newman

THE **BOBBS-MERRILL** COMPANY, INC.
A SUBSIDIARY OF HOWARD W. SAMS & CO., INC.
Publishers · INDIANAPOLIS · NEW YORK

LIBRARY OF CONGRESS CATALOG CARD NUMBER: 60-14836

PRINTED IN THE UNITED STATES OF AMERICA

For Ida, Jack, Paula, Jeff, and Pete

The author gratefully acknowledges the help of Mary Andersen, who was born on the island of Maui.

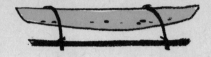

Illustrations

Full pages

Numerous smaller illustrations

Contents

CHILDHOOD
OF FAMOUS
AMERICANS

★ # Liliuokalani

Young Hawaiian Queen

The King's Present

ONE MORNING in 1842 a chubby four-year-old girl was waking up in a large grass house in Honolulu, Hawaii. Her name was Liliuokalani, but everyone called her Lydia. Her father was a high-ranking Hawaiian chief, just as her grandfather and great-grandfather had been.

A man and woman were leaning over Lydia's bed. They were Papa Paki and Mama Konia, her parents by adoption.

It was the custom among Hawaiian chiefs to give their newborn babies to other chiefs to raise. The chiefs believed that this custom made them feel as close as if they all belonged to one big family. Lydia often saw her real father and mother, but she felt closer to Papa Paki, Mama Konia, and their daughter Bernice.

Mama Konia smoothed back Lydia's dark, wavy hair. "She seems so little to start school," she said in Hawaiian.

"School!" The word woke Lydia as completely as a splash of cold ocean water would have done. "Do I start to school now?" she cried.

Papa Paki swung her high in the air. Then he lowered her to his face for a rub-nose kiss. "Not today, Lydia," he said. "The missionary-teacher will come this afternoon to see whether you are old enough. Hurry now! The King is taking you and your sister Bernice for a ride in his canoe this morning."

"Goody! His canoe is so big!" Lydia cried. Then her forehead wrinkled. "What is it like at school, Papa Paki?"

Papa Paki set her down on the earth floor. "All

the Hawaiian princes and princesses go to the Royal School to learn to speak English," he said. "Hawaii must learn the modern ways of other countries. You are not a princess like Bernice, but you are of royal blood. You must learn, too. Who knows? Even you could be called upon to rule our people someday!"

Bernice, whom Lydia called "sister," was Papa Paki's real daughter. She was a princess because her great-grandfather had been the first King of Hawaii. Lydia's great-grandfather had just been a cousin of that king.

"Where is Bernice?" Lydia asked now. She ran to the door. She did not see Bernice, but she saw her nurse hurrying toward the house. The nurse's name was Kaikai. She was very tall and fat. As she ran across the yard, the skirt of her long yellow dress fluttered about her ankles. She picked Lydia up and wrapped her in a piece of blue cloth.

"I'm going for a ride in the King's canoe today!" Lydia cried.

"Good!" Kaikai placed a string of pink and white flowers around Lydia's neck. "Here is a special lei for your ride! Hurry outside now and eat your breakfast!"

Lydia went out to the yard.

"Aloha! Good morning, sleepyhead!" Eleven-year-old Bernice sat under a tall palm tree, eating. She, too, wore a bright piece of cloth wrapped around her. Her long hair fell softly about her bare shoulders.

"She is the prettiest sister in all Hawaii," Lydia thought. She ran over and took a piece of melon from the wooden bowl Kaikai set on a mat for her. "I might go to school with you tomorrow," she said between bites.

"I know." Bernice passed Lydia some fish. "It would be fun to have you at school with me, little sister. If you come, though, you must not bother

me there. Now that my vacation is over, I have much work to do!"

"I hope I can go!" Lydia drank some coconut milk from the shell. Then she skipped around the yard and hummed a little tune.

"You make such nice songs, Lydia," Kaikai said. She took Lydia's hand and started down a path toward the ocean. Bernice walked along beside them. Bright-colored birds flew among the palms. The morning air was sweet with the odor of blossoms.

"Look!" Kaikai pointed her plump finger at the high mountains around Honolulu. They looked dark and purple against the sky. "It's raining over there," she said, "but it is fine by the ocean. See, there's a rainbow!"

"I can see all the colors," Bernice said. "Red, orange——"

"Perhaps one of our old gods will slide down and pay us a visit today!" Kaikai threw her head back and laughed.

"Did you ever really believe the gods slid down the rainbows?" Bernice asked.

"Yes, many years ago, before the missionaries came. They taught us it was not true."

Lydia jumped up and down. "I'd like to slide down a rainbow, but how could I ever climb high enough? I'd keep slipping back!"

She saw her friend Victoria in front of a grass

16

house by the side of the path. Victoria was the same age as Lydia. The long braids hung down on either side of her dainty face.

"Aloha! Good morning!" Lydia called.

"Aloha!" Victoria answered. Her big brothers, Moses, Lot, and Alexander, were in the yard playing a bowling-game with round, smooth stones. They looked up and waved.

"Victoria can come, but no boys!" Bernice told them firmly.

Lydia and Victoria skipped gaily toward the waterfront. "The teacher is coming to my house to see whether I'm big enough for school," Lydia told Victoria excitedly.

"She's coming to see us, too. I hope we can both go." Victoria pointed toward the beach. "Look, there's the King."

Four tall poles with bright yellow feathers on top were staked in the sand. These feathered poles meant the King was near by.

17

Lydia smiled happily. All the Hawaiian people loved their King. He walked up the beach toward the girls. He was dressed in a wide piece of cloth about his thighs and waist. His tanned body glistened in the sun. The gold bracelets on his arms jangled.

"Aloha! Good morning!" he called.

Everyone bowed.

The King smiled at Lydia and Victoria. "Your fathers tell me you might be starting to the Royal School tomorrow. Good! Are you ready for your ride this morning?"

He clapped his hands together, and four servant-boys lifted a big canoe to their shoulders. With long strides, they carried it across the sand into the water. The canoe was really the hollowed-out trunk of a great tree. It had an extra piece of wood attached to the outside, called an "outrigger." This kept the boat steady even in rough water.

The King's brown eyes twinkled. "Perhaps a trading ship in the harbor will have something nice for all of you," he said. "Come! We shall go out to see."

Lydia bubbled with excitement as she ran down to the water and climbed into the canoe beside Victoria. Kaikai and Bernice sat behind them. The King took his place in the front of the boat, and one of his servant-boys placed a yellow feathered cape about his bare shoulders. Then the servants dipped their long paddles into the sparkling water.

At first, the front of the canoe disappeared in a great wave. Then the canoe rose and skimmed over the water. Soon it turned into the harbor entrance. The children hardly knew which way to look first.

There were dozens of big trading ships and whaling vessels anchored in the harbor. The flags of many countries flew from their masts.

The decks of the ships were much higher than the canoe, so the children could not see the men on board. However, they could hear their voices.

"Here comes the King!" someone called as the canoe came close to an American ship.

"I will go on board," the King said. He took hold of the rope ladder that hung over the side of the ship. "You children wait here in the canoe. Perhaps I shall have that surprise when I return." The ladder swayed back and forth under his weight, but he was soon at the top.

Bernice leaned over to talk to Lydia and Victoria. "Our harbor is so crowded!" she said. "Sometimes I think you could go all the way across the harbor by jumping from one ship to another. Look! See the boys diving for coins!"

The men on the ships were throwing shiny coins into the ocean. Young boys dived into the water from their canoes. Soon they came up with the coins between their strong, white teeth.

"I think I'll try that!" Lydia looked back at Kaikai and grinned. "Well, when I'm bigger I will. Oh, here comes the King!"

The King came down the ladder. His long legs took two steps at a time. He tossed three packages into the canoe. Then he sat down and motioned the boys to start back.

The boys paddled out of the harbor and along the shore. Lydia stared at the packages the whole time. "What do you think is in them?" she whispered to Victoria.

Bernice patted her on the shoulder. "Just wait and see," she said.

The servant-boys paddled very fast until they reached some big waves that carried the canoe right up onto the beach. When the children had scrambled out of the canoe, the King gave each of them a package.

"Thank you, Your Majesty." Bernice sat down on the sand and opened hers first. She smiled with delight. It was a piece of red cloth from which her mother could make her a new dress.

Before the missionaries came, Hawaiian girls had always worn a piece of cloth wrapped around them, just as the girls were wearing today. The missionaries made them long dresses to wear to school. Soon all the Hawaiian women were wearing dresses on important occasions.

Now Victoria tore away the paper on her gift. It was a big rag doll! "Oh, thank you!" she cried, hugging it tightly.

Lydia squeezed her package. What could it be? It felt too hard to be cloth like Bernice's, or a rag doll like Victoria's. Quickly, she tore off the paper. It was a queer wooden thing with strings on it! She looked up at the King, puzzled.

"It is called a guitar, Lydia," he said. "The traders say it makes music. See?" He plucked one of the strings with his thumb, and it made a twanging sound. "I have often heard you make up songs," he went on. "Perhaps someday you will make up a song for me!"

Lydia squealed with delight. "Thank you! I will learn to play it, Your Majesty," she said seriously. "Someday I *will* make up a song just for you, and I'll play it on my guitar."

Kaikai took her hand. "Come, children," she said. "We must go home now. It is almost time for the missionary-teacher's visit."

The Royal School

Lydia and Bernice ran into the grass house. Lydia waved her guitar excitedly. "Mama Konia! Papa Paki! See what the King gave me!"

Then she stopped short and flushed. A strange woman in a dark dress sat at the table. Her eyeglasses shone in the sunlight that streamed in through the door.

"You must be Lydia," the woman said in Hawaiian. "Come closer. I want to see you."

Lydia hesitated. Then she saw Papa Paki and Mama Konia on the other side of the room.

"This is Mrs. Cooke," Bernice said. "She is the teacher at the Royal Boarding School."

"Oh." Lydia's voice was shaky. Would she be big enough to go? Shyly, she crossed the earth floor. Now she could see the hairpins that held Mrs. Cooke's hair in a bun at the back of her head. "I wonder if they hurt," she thought.

The teacher was looking down at Lydia's bare feet. She pursed her lips. "At school, we wear shoes," she said.

"I shall buy her some at the trader's today," Papa Paki answered.

Lydia put one foot over the other, self-consciously. Then she braced her shoulders. She stood as straight and tall as she could. "Am I big enough?" she asked. She clutched her guitar tightly as if it might bring her luck.

"We'll see." Mrs. Cooke looked Lydia over from the tip of her bare toes to the top of her dark hair. "Do you want to go to school?"

"Oh, yes! I must learn to speak English!"

The teacher stood up and straightened the folds in her skirt. She walked over and spoke quietly to Papa Paki.

Lydia strained her ears, but she could not hear what they said. She looked at Bernice, but Bernice just smiled.

Finally Mrs. Cooke spoke. "Have her there tomorrow morning at eight o'clock," she said. "I must go to see Victoria now. Good-by, children. Remember, we are not late at school!"

Papa Paki and Bernice went outside to show

the teacher the way to Victoria's house. Lydia climbed up on Mama Konia's lap. She plucked at the strings of her guitar.

"Victoria's smaller than I am. It would be awful if she couldn't go to school, too," she sighed. "Why doesn't Mrs. Cooke smile more?"

Mama Konia spoke slowly. "These missionary women from the United States have done much for our islands. They are good people, but laughter does not come so easily to them as it does to us." She set Lydia down and picked up the quilt she was making.

Another missionary woman had taught Mama Konia how to sew, and Papa Paki had bought special yellow cloth for the quilt.

"Run outside and play now," Mama Konia said. "I must finish this, so you can take it to school with you tomorrow."

As Lydia lay on her bed of soft mats that night, she wondered what tomorrow would be like. It would seem funny not to live here with Papa Paki and Mama Konia. She glanced at her sister. "I am glad Bernice will be there, too," she thought sleepily.

The Royal Boarding School was not far from Lydia's home, but Kaikai carried her there on her shoulders the next morning. Lydia was wearing her new shoes, and the path was muddy.

"You look very grown-up in your new long dress," Kaikai said.

Lydia ducked her head under some palm leaves. "It's just like Bernice's. Kaikai, why did Bernice leave for school before we did?"

Kaikai hesitated. There was a twinkle in her dark eyes. "Oh, she had some work to do. She went ahead with the servants who carried your things. You will see her soon."

"Well, hurry, Kaikai." Lydia playfully imitated Mrs. Cooke's words. "Remember, we are not late at school!"

They turned into the entrance of the Royal School. Kaikai set Lydia down on the ground. Lydia looked around curiously. A high brick wall cast a deep shadow over four small American-style cottages, arranged around a courtyard. Everything was quiet. No one was about.

Suddenly a feeling of loneliness welled up inside Lydia. She threw her arms around Kaikai and buried her face in the folds of Kaikai's skirt.

"Don't leave me! Take me home!" she sobbed. "I want to go home to Papa Paki!"

Kaikai knelt down and kissed her. "The daughter of a chief does not cry," she said gently. "See! Here comes Bernice! Victoria, too!"

"Aloha! Aloha!" Bernice, Victoria, and Victoria's three brothers came running out of the house. When they saw Lydia's tear-stained face, they led her around to the back.

"W—where are you taking me?" Lydia cried. "I want to go—go home to Papa Paki."

"Look, Lydia!" Bernice boosted her up so that she could see over a fence. Through her tears, Lydia saw a white goat. It was hitched to a shiny red cart with big wheels. There was a puffy pillow on the seat of the cart. Lydia had seen goats before, but never one with such a long, straggly beard as this one had.

"That's the real reason I came so early," Bernice explained. "Papa Paki bought you the cart. I wanted to get Nanny hitched up for you."

Lydia and Victoria scrambled through the gate and climbed into the cart. Lydia wiped away her tears and took hold of the reins. She did not even notice that Kaikai had left.

"Don't let the goat come on this side of the fence," Bernice warned. "Goats love to eat flowers. Mrs. Cooke has a geranium plant here that her brother sent from the United States."

"We won't." Around and around the yard Lydia and Victoria rode. Every time they passed the gate, the other children called to them. Suddenly, they heard the shrill sound of a whistle.

Bernice came through the gate and caught hold of the goat's bridle. "We must go in now," she told the girls.

Lydia and Victoria climbed down from the cart. Lydia patted the goat between the ears. "I'll see you later, Nanny. I have to do my schoolwork now!"

She went into the house with the other children. The classroom was bright and cheery, with crisp white curtains at the windows. The ceilings were much higher than the ceilings at home.

Mrs. Cooke looked up from her big desk at the front of the room. "Good morning," she said, her blue eyes sparkling behind her glasses. "I see our two new pupils are here."

Lydia and Victoria did not understand, for Mrs. Cooke spoke in English, but together they answered, "Aloha!"

Lydia took a seat between Bernice and Victoria. She looked around at the other children. Including herself, there were eight in all. She knew Bernice, Victoria, and Victoria's three brothers, Moses, Lot, and Alexander. There were also two other boys, David and William. Later on Lydia learned that David was her real brother, who had been adopted by another chief.

Mrs. Cooke tapped on her desk with a pencil. "We shall begin by singing a hymn. Please turn to page three in your book."

The hymn sounded very different from the swaying Hawaiian rhythms that Lydia knew so well, but she liked it. At first, she could not read the words, so she just hummed along with the others. By that afternoon, however, she had already learned some of the English words in her book. She did not feel homesick again until that night, when she sat at the supper table with the other children.

Mrs. Cooke passed a dish of bread.

Lydia took some. She bit off a small piece and chewed it slowly. This was the first time she had ever tasted bread. At home her family always ate poi instead. Poi is a mixture made from the roots of a plant. The Hawaiian people loved their poi.

Mrs. Cooke smiled when she saw how slowly Lydia was eating. "Perhaps this will make it taste better." She poured plenty of thick molasses on Lydia's bread.

"It's nice and sweet," Lydia said as she took another bite. She still wished she had some poi.

When supper was over, everyone went upstairs. Lydia and Victoria were glad they were going to sleep together. They looked curiously around their room.

"Such high things to sleep on!" Lydia cried, bouncing up and down on her bed. She lay back and looked up at the flowered wallpaper. How different from the green cloth that covered the walls at home! "Mrs. Cooke must really love flowers!" she giggled. "She even has them all over the walls!"

Just then the teacher came in. "No more laughing, girls. Good night." She blew out the lamp and left.

"Crosspatch!" Victoria wailed. "She won't even let us laugh."

Lydia remembered what Mama Konia had said. "Laughter does not come so easily to these missionary women as it does to us." She yawned. "It would be nice to see Mrs. Cooke laugh, really laugh," she said, covering herself with the quilt Mama Konia had made. She was glad she had it. It made her feel more at home.

A few days later, Lydia and Victoria were riding around the yard in the goat-cart. Suddenly, the animal poked his head outside the open gate. He nibbled at something on the ground. It was

Mrs. Cooke's geranium plant, the one her brother had sent from the United States!

Lydia tugged at the reins.

At that very moment, Mrs. Cooke looked out the window. Her hair was wet and fell loosely around her face. Lydia knew she was washing it.

"You miserable goat!" the teacher cried. "Stop eating my plant! Lydia! Victoria! Take her inside that gate at once! I must dry my hair." She shut the window with a bang.

Lydia scolded the goat. "That is a naughty thing to do!" she cried. "Stop!"

The goat went on eating until only a few chewed-up leaves were left.

Lydia's eyes flashed. She pulled the goat inside the gate. "That plant made Mrs. Cooke feel more at home!" she cried. "Like—like my quilt! You are a bad, bad goat!" Then she began to laugh. Nanny looked so funny with pink petals all over her beard!

Suddenly, Lydia had an idea. Maybe if Mrs. Cooke laughed, really laughed, she wouldn't feel so bad about her plant.

"Victoria," she said breathlessly, "please go to our room and get that piece of red cloth lying on my dresser."

"What for?"

"You'll see. Quick now. I'll meet you here in the yard."

While Victoria hurried into the house, Lydia ran to the classroom. She got a pencil and a piece of paper and went in search of Bernice. When she returned to the yard, Victoria was already there with the piece of cloth.

Quickly, Lydia unfolded the cloth and grabbed hold of the goat. "Hold still, Nanny," she said and began to wrap the cloth around the goat's middle.

The goat bleated loudly.

Lydia stroked the goat's neck. "We won't hurt

38

you," she said. "We're just trying to make you pretty for Mrs. Cooke."

Victoria giggled. "She looks like——"

"A Hawaiian goat!" Lydia finished. Her eyes sparkled with merriment. "Instead of Nanny, your name is Nalani now," she said to the goat.

She picked up the piece of paper that she had taken from the classroom. "Listen," she said. "I had Bernice write this in English.

> " 'I'm very sorry I ate your flower,
> Because it tasted very sour.
> Nalani' "

Victoria looked at the paper over Lydia's shoulder. She started to laugh. Then she said, "Maybe that will make Mrs. Cooke angry."

"I don't think so," Lydia said. "Give me your lei, please."

Victoria looked puzzled, but took the flower lei from around her neck.

Lydia poked a hole in the top of the paper. She slipped the paper over the lei. Then she placed the lei over the goat's head.

The animal just looked at her through half-closed eyes.

"Quick! Here comes Mrs. Cooke now!" Lydia pulled Victoria behind a tree.

Mrs. Cooke came across the yard. Her damp hair clung to the sides of her head. Her mouth was set in a straight line. She leaned over and looked closely at her geranium plant. Then she stood up straight and shook her finger angrily at the goat.

"You bad Nanny!" she said.

Lydia held her breath. Maybe it wasn't such a good idea after all!

Mrs. Cooke saw the lei and came through the gate. She frowned and pulled the paper off the lei. Her lips moved as she read the words.

Victoria squeezed Lydia's arm.

Suddenly the lines between Mrs. Cooke's eyes disappeared. The corners of her mouth turned up. She was smiling!

Lydia and Victoria jumped out from behind the tree. They were both laughing.

"All right, children," the teacher said. "I guess my geranium wasn't as pretty as your Hawaiian flowers anyway. 'Flower and sour.' Land sakes, Lydia, what kind of a rhyme is that?"

Bare Feet at Church

"Hurry, Lydia!" Bernice poked her head through the doorway of Lydia's room. "Everyone else is ready to go."

"How do I look?" Lydia stood in front of the mirror. She had on a white dress. It came clear to her ankles. She had new shoes to match, and she wore a wreath of white flowers on her head.

She was seven years old. Today she was to sing in the children's choir at church. Papa Paki, Mama Konia, the King—everyone would be there to hear her.

Bernice gave Lydia's hair a pat. "You look fine," she said. " We are all so proud that you

42

have been chosen. Hurry, now. Everyone but you is ready to leave."

Lydia followed Bernice down the stairs. Mrs. Cooke was lining the children up in the court-yard. They were all dressed in their Sunday best. The girls wore gay dresses. The boys had on blue uniforms trimmed with shiny gold braid. Mrs. Cooke wore a lace collar on her dress.

"Oh, there you are," the teacher called. "Bernice, you and Lot are the oldest. You shall head the procession."

Bernice's dimples deepened as she took her place beside Lot, Victoria's brother. Lydia and Victoria were still the youngest children at school, so they marched together at the end of the line.

"Are you scared?" Victoria asked, running her fingers over the red ribbons in her braids.

"Scared of what?" asked Lydia.

Victoria was surprised that Lydia didn't know

what there was to be scared of. "Of singing in the choir, of course! Won't you be shaky? All those people watching you?"

"Oh, that's nothing!"

Mrs. Cooke walked back and forth. She was making sure that everyone looked perfect. "David, tie your shoe," she said. "All right! Remember, everyone, no laughing or playing in church today!"

Mrs. Cooke led them out of the courtyard. Then they went down the path and onto King Street. Many people watched the children.

"Hurrah for Prince Alexander!" they called. "Hurrah for Princess Bernice! Hurrah for the High Chief's daughter!"

By now Lydia knew why Bernice was a princess and she was only a High Chief's daughter. Bernice's great-grandfather, Kamehameha I, had set up the kingdom of Hawaii, and Bernice herself might become Queen someday. Since Lydia's great-grandfather had only been a cousin of Kamehameha, Lydia would probably never become Queen. When a king died, the throne passed on to his closest relative.

"I must always serve the King and the people of Hawaii, though," Lydia thought as she nodded and smiled at the crowd.

She walked on tiptoe and looked at the church up ahead. It was surrounded by tall trees. Its white coral blocks gleamed in the sun. The coral had been cut from the reef along the ocean.

There were no trucks in Hawaii in those days. The people had hauled every block of coral by cart. How proud they had been of their new church! It was a sign of the progress that Hawaii was making. Lydia and Bernice were especially proud, for Papa Paki had brought the first block. It had weighed half a ton.

The royal children walked quickly up the church steps. Many people crowded around the entrance. Lydia and Victoria were about to go inside when Lydia happened to glance back. She saw a girl sitting on the ground by the bottom step. She was just about Lydia's age. Her head was buried in her arms, and her shoulders were shaking. She was crying!

"Why should she be crying?" Lydia whispered to Victoria. "I'm going to see——"

"The choir, Lydia! They're waiting for you!"

Lydia peeked inside the church. She looked down at the King's pew. She could see the yellow feathers of his cape. He was already there.

"I must see what's wrong with that girl," she thought. She ran back down the stairs.

She touched the girl's shoulder. "Why are you crying?" she asked.

The girl did not look up. She pointed a trembling finger at the doorkeeper. "He won't let me in the church," she sobbed. "I—I have no shoes." Then she raised her head.

"Oh, that's too bad," Lydia said, looking down at the girl's feet. "I wish I could give you mine, but I'm singing in the choir today."

She stopped. "The doorkeeper always looks to see if the *poor* children have shoes," she thought. "I have never seen him look down at the feet of the royal children. He knows we have them. Maybe——"

She glanced quickly around to make sure that

47

no one was watching. Then she knelt down and unbuckled her shoes. She placed them in the girl's hands.

"W—what will you do?" the girl asked.

"I have an idea. Quick! Put them on!"

The girl slipped her feet into the shoes and stood up.

"Walk in front of me," Lydia said. They started up the stairs. The doorkeeper had been leaning against one of the tall, white columns. Now he stepped in front of the door. He looked puzzled as he glanced down at the other girl's feet. Then he stepped aside and let her pass. His eyes were on Lydia's face now.

"Aloha," she said with a bright smile.

"Oh, it's you!" He scratched his head thoughtfully. "I thought I saw you go in before."

"I'm a little late," she answered. Somehow she had to keep him from looking at her feet. She reached up and pulled one of the flowers from

48

the wreath in her hair. She placed it in his hand and stepped inside. She held her breath until she heard the door close behind her.

The whole church was decorated with sweet-smelling flowers and shiny leaves. They hung down from the ceiling and twined around the tall pillars. The church was crowded, and the girl had taken a seat in the back row. She smiled her thanks to Lydia.

There was a rustle of excitement. The children in the choir were standing in the front of the church. They were almost ready to sing. Lydia ran down the aisle. She saw Mrs. Cooke turn around in her seat and motion her to hurry.

"I'm supposed to stand in front," Lydia thought as she reached the front of the church. "If I do, everyone will see my feet!" She squeezed between two girls in the middle of the group. One of them started to say something, but Lydia pretended not to hear.

The leader raised his hands. Lydia and the other children in the choir began to sing.

Lydia looked around the church. Papa Paki and Mama Konia were smiling proudly. The King nodded his head in approval. Mrs. Cooke's lips moved as she sang the hymn to herself. As Lydia stood on tiptoe, she saw the girl in the back row. The girl looked very happy, and that made Lydia feel happy, too.

The choir finished, and Lydia ran to her seat beside Mrs. Cooke. Quickly, she tucked her feet under her long dress.

The teacher picked up the bottom of her skirt. "Where are your shoes?" she whispered. Lydia could tell that she was trying her best not to speak out loud.

"I—I gave them to a girl. She was crying because the doorkeeper wouldn't let her in——" Lydia began.

Mrs. Cooke's blue eyes widened in surprise.

Then she patted Lydia's hand briskly. "Next time, take an extra pair of shoes with you." She sat back and straightened her black bonnet on her head. "What would my friends in New England say? My pupil, singing in church with bare feet! Sh!" she said, as if Lydia were doing the talking. "Reverend Armstrong is about to begin his sermon!"

The Boy Next Door

A FEW months later, Lydia and Victoria were in the courtyard of the Royal Boarding School. They were playing "cat's cradle" with a string. Victoria slipped the string from Lydia's hands to her own. "That's fun," she said.

Suddenly, they heard a noise. They looked toward the high brick wall that separated the Royal School from the day school next door. A boy had just jumped off the wall. He had light hair and skin, and many freckles across his nose. He looked at the girls curiously.

"Aloha!" Lydia said. Then, in English, she asked, "What's your name?"

"Johnny Dominis." He cocked his head to one
side. "Are you a princess?"

"No, but my sister is. I'm the daughter of a
High Chief," Lydia said proudly.

"Pooh! What's so special about that?" he said. "My father's the captain of a big ship! I'll bet I can do anything you can do!"

Lydia slipped the cat's cradle back from Victoria's hands to her own without spoiling it. "Can you do that?" she asked.

Johnny slipped the cat's cradle from Lydia's hands to his. "There." He grinned.

Lydia thought for a minute. Then she reached into the pocket Mrs. Cooke had sewn on her dress. She pulled out a small rubber ball and five pebbles. Sitting on the ground, she spread the five pebbles out before her. Then she threw the ball up in the air. Before it bounced, she scooped up three of the pebbles.

"Anyone can do that," Johnny said. He sat down and threw the ball into the air. Before it bounced, he scooped up all the pebbles.

"I have to do something really hard," Lydia thought. She ran to the other side of the court-

54

yard and picked up two sticks. "I can make a fire! I've seen my Papa Paki do it!" She waved the sticks in the air.

"I bet you can't," Johnny said.

"I can!" Lydia crouched near the ground. Holding the sticks firmly, she rubbed them back and forth against each other.

"Mrs. Cooke'll see you!" Victoria cried. "You know she told us never to start fires."

Lydia was too busy to think about Mrs. Cooke. She rubbed and rubbed. She bent her head close to the sticks and blew off some powdery stuff. She rubbed harder, faster. All at once the sticks began to smoke.

"Here comes Mrs. Cooke!" Victoria cried.

Lydia dropped the sticks and stamped on them. "She must have seen us through the window," she said.

Johnny motioned the girls to follow him to some tall shrubs at the back of the goat's yard.

One by one, they all squeezed through. When they got to the other side, they looked around. They were in a big garden with sweet-smelling flowers and tall, broad-topped trees.

"We'd better go back," Lydia said. She bent over to watch an orange butterfly light on a white ginger blossom.

Victoria pointed to a large stone house on the other side of the wide lawn. "Look! That's my aunt's house. I never came to it this way before." Her voice dropped to a whisper. "Sh! I hear someone coming."

They all stood still, listening to the padding of footsteps on the grass. The sound seemed to come from the other side of some big trees.

"Mrs. Cooke!" Lydia thought. "She must have come around the other way!" She placed her finger over her lips in a signal for Victoria and Johnny to be quiet. Then she saw a tall Hawaiian woman come out from behind a tree.

"It's my aunt!" Victoria shouted.

"Why, Victoria, dear!" her aunt said in surprise. "What are you doing here? You're not supposed to leave school grounds."

"We were just——"

"I know." Victoria's aunt playfully tugged at Victoria's braids. "You were exploring." She handed each of them a piece of coconut candy from a basket over her arm. "Go along now," she said. "Mrs. Cooke will be looking for you."

"Thank you!" Lydia, Victoria, and Johnny munched on the candy as they slipped back through the bushes. Johnny ran toward the wall and scampered over the top.

Lydia was worried about what Mrs. Cooke would do when they got back. The teacher smiled more now, but she probably would not smile this time. Lydia had not only started a fire, but she and Victoria had run away, too!

"Lydia! Victoria!" It was Mrs. Cooke's voice.

Lydia held her breath as the teacher came running toward them. "Where have you been?" she called, waving her arms excitedly. "I've just received permission to take all of you to the King's meeting with the people."

Lydia and Victoria looked at each other quickly. Did Mrs. Cooke mean she had told the King that Lydia had tried to light a fire?

Mrs. Cooke was smiling. She wasn't talking about the fire at all. "This is the first time the people of the islands will have a chance to talk over their troubles with their King," she said. "He sent word that we could come and watch. It shows how much and how quickly the people of Hawaii are learning."

"She didn't even see me try to light the fire," Lydia thought. "She just came out to tell us about the meeting."

The teacher bent over to look at them closely. "My goodness, how did you two get so dirty?"

Lydia hesitated.

Victoria shut her lips tightly, as if to say, "Don't tell her anything."

"Uh—we'll get cleaned up right away!" Lydia cried. "Come on, Victoria." The girls ran into the house and up to their room.

Victoria splashed water on her face. "Whew! It's a good thing she didn't make us tell."

"Yes," Lydia said. "She'd punish me for sure. She'd probably make me go to bed right after supper tonight."

"That wouldn't be any fun. You usually play your guitar and sing with the rest of us then."

"That's the best part of the whole day," Lydia said. "It *is* a good thing we didn't tell."

All the way to the King's meeting, however, Lydia felt funny inside.

The King's Meeting

THERE WAS a big hill in the middle of Honolulu. Once it had been a volcano, spitting forth smoke and huge rivers of lava, or melted rock, but it was no longer active. It was shaped like an upside-down bowl, so it was called "Punchbowl." The King's meeting was held in a hall built at the foot of Punchbowl.

As Lydia sat down inside the hall, she looked around curiously. She was excited, but whenever she remembered how she had tried to light a fire, she got that funny feeling again.

A tall, golden throne had been placed in the center of a platform at one end of the hall. It was for the King. He had not yet come, but many men in uniform sat around the throne. An old man with bent shoulders stood at one side of the platform. Lydia noticed that his clothes were old and worn.

She turned to Mrs. Cooke and whispered, "Who are those men in uniforms?"

"The King's advisers," the teacher explained. "They are from the United States. They help him and give him advice."

Lydia did not have a chance to ask about the old man in the worn-out clothes. Suddenly, there was a loud noise outside.

"That's the cannon from the fort next door," Mrs. Cooke said. "A twenty-one gun salute is being fired in honor of the King."

Everyone stood up and faced the entrance. The King marched in. He wore a dark uniform and a beautiful cape of yellow feathers. A gleaming sword hung at his side.

"How different he looks when we see him on the beach," Lydia thought.

The High Chiefs marched in behind the King. They, too, wore splendid uniforms. They had shorter feathered capes around their shoulders.

"There's Papa Paki!" Lydia waved as he passed down the aisle. He smiled but did not wave back.

Now the King climbed the steps to the platform and stood before his throne. A hush fell over the audience. The flag of Hawaii was raised. It was blue, red, and white, and it had eight stripes.

"The stripes stand for the eight islands of Hawaii," Lydia whispered to Victoria, who was sitting beside her.

Lydia did not take her eyes off the flag. It rose slowly until it almost touched the ceiling. "I always feel good when I see the flag," she thought. Everything was so exciting that she almost forgot about trying to light the fire.

The King raised his hand. There was a rustle of excitement as everyone sat down.

Lydia leaned forward eagerly. What a sight! The King sat on his great throne. Beside and behind him were the fair-skinned men from the United States and Papa Paki and the other High Chiefs. Over them all hung the flag. It was a grand sight.

The old man with the worn-out clothes was brought before the King.

"Who is he?" Lydia asked.

"He has done something wrong," Mrs. Cooke answered. "Watch!"

The man shifted nervously on his bare feet. "I stole my neighbor's chicken." He spoke so softly that Lydia could hardly hear him.

"Why did you steal?" the King asked. His voice sounded deep compared with the old man's.

"I—I——" The man took a deep breath and started over again. "Your Majesty, I live in the

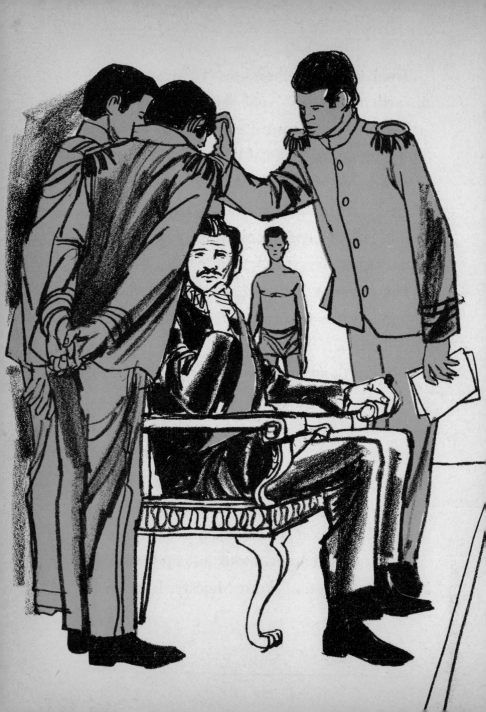

mountains, far from the ocean. There are no streams or lakes near us. I cannot catch fish. No rain has fallen for many days. My crops are poor. My family was hungry."

"You did something wrong," the King said solemnly. "You must be punished so you will remember not to do it again. That is justice. My advisers and I will decide what your punishment is to be."

He leaned back on his throne. His advisers gathered around him. They all spoke quietly together for a long time. No one could hear what they said. The old man waited on the other side of the platform. He turned his straw hat around and around in his hands.

Lydia turned to Mrs. Cooke. "What will they do to him?" she asked in a low voice.

"I don't know, but you heard what the King said. He must be punished."

The funny feeling inside Lydia grew stronger.

"M—Mrs. Cooke, I tried to light a fire with two sticks!" The words rushed out before Lydia could stop them. She heard Victoria gasp.

The teacher's eyes widened. "You could have hurt yourself, Lydia," she whispered. "You are a good girl to tell me, but you must remember not to do it again. You shall go to bed right after supper every night for a week."

"Yes, ma'am," Lydia said weakly.

The King rose from his throne. "This man shall stay in the Honolulu jail for the rest of this day. When he goes home, he shall give his neighbor two chickens."

Lydia caught her breath. That poor man! How could he? He didn't have any chickens.

The King was speaking again. "None of my people should be hungry," he said. "My servants will bring you chickens to take home with you."

A bright smile lighted the man's wrinkled face. "Thank you, Your Majesty!" he cried.

Everyone in the hall clapped.

"If I were a queen, I'd have done the same thing the King did," Lydia said to Victoria.

"What if you were a teacher? Would you have done the same thing Mrs. Cooke did?"

Lydia hesitated. Then she answered, "Yes, I guess I would."

A Trip to a Volcano

It was vacation time. Lydia was eight. She and some of the other children from the Royal Boarding School were on the deck of the King's yacht. They were taking a trip to Hawaii, the largest of all the Hawaiian Islands.

"Look!" cried Lydia. She pointed toward shore. "That must be the volcano. There's smoke coming from that mountain!"

"Yes, that's vapor from Kilauea," said Kaikai, who had come along to take care of Lydia. "Tomorrow night, we shall be standing on the rim of the crater. Then we shall see the fire."

Lydia gasped. "The only volcanoes I've ever

seen are Punchbowl and Diamond Head, but they never erupt."

Victoria squeezed to the railing beside her. She drew her dark eyebrows together. "Won't it be dangerous?" she asked.

"Not if you don't stand too close to the edge. It would take many days for the crater to fill up enough to overflow. Even then, the lava moves so slowly there would be plenty of time to get out of the way."

Everyone stared at the gray vapor rising from the great mountain. It reminded Lydia of the puffs of smoke Papa Paki blew from his pipe. She could hardly wait till tomorrow night.

The royal party spent the night in the city of Hilo. They started up to the volcano on horse-back the next morning. The King rode ahead with the guides. Lydia and Victoria shared a big black horse toward the end of the line. They followed a narrow path through a thick jungle.

"Look at those tall ferns!" Lydia called back to Kaikai. "They're even taller than you."

Lydia leaned back in the saddle and looked up. The jungle was so thick that she could barely see patches of blue sky peeping through the leaves. Flocks of birds hummed around the red blossoms of the tall trees.

Suddenly she squinted. Was there something else in one of those trees? It could not be a monkey, for there were no monkeys in Hawaii. Then she saw that it was a man crawling out on a branch high above the ground.

"That man is a royal feather-gatherer," Kaikai explained. "Look, he's smearing some sticky stuff on the branches. That is to hold the birds when they light in the tree."

Now the man slid down the trunk of the tree to the ground. Everyone stopped and looked up.

"I feel like scaring the birds away, so they won't get caught," Lydia whispered to Victoria.

"You'd better not!"

"I think it's awful to catch those poor little things." Just the same, Lydia held the reins tightly so that the horse would not move.

Several birds fluttered about in the leaves. One by one, they alighted on the sticky branches. Six of them lined up side by side. Then they began to flap their wings wildly.

"They're trying to get away!" Lydia cried.

The man scampered back up the tree. He climbed out on a branch just above the birds. His big hand reached down, raised the wing of one bird, and plucked a small feather.

"What's he doing that for?" Lydia cried.

The man placed the feather in a satchel over his shoulder. Then he lifted the bird off the sticky stuff. He held it high in the air and opened his hand. The bird flew away.

Lydia caught her breath. "He didn't hurt it! He let it go!"

"Yes, he let it go," Kaikai said. "He takes one little feather from each bird. These are the feathers used in the capes of the King and the High Chiefs. They are the symbol, or sign, of Hawaiian royalty."

"Well, I'm glad he doesn't hurt the birds to get the feathers."

The party went on to a village halfway up the side of the mountain.

"We stop here for lunch," Kaikai said.

Lydia and Victoria slid off their horse.

"It feels so good to stretch my legs," Lydia cried. She ran toward a tree covered with feathery clusters of red and yellow flowers. "Come on," she called to Victoria. "Let's pick some flowers. We'll make leis."

"Stop, Lydia!" Kaikai cried. "Don't pick any of those flowers!"

"Why not? They're growing wild."

"They are special flowers," said the nurse. "If you pick them on the way up a mountain, it will surely rain. That would spoil our trip!" Kaikai looked serious, but her eyes twinkled.

"Then we'll pick them on our way back," Lydia agreed. "I wouldn't want anything to happen to keep me from seeing that volcano."

After lunch, the party started on the last lap of the trip. The horses picked their way slowly across a slippery field of black lava.

"There are so many waves and bumps in this lava that it looks as if it were a frozen black ocean," Lydia said.

"It is very hot down in the volcano," Kaikai said. "When the lava comes out, it is so hot that it is molten, or liquid. It flows like the thick molasses you sometimes have at school. It looks like waves now because it was moving in ripples and waves when it cooled off and hardened."

Suddenly the horse that Lydia and Victoria were riding stumbled over one of the waves. Victoria, who was riding in front now, clung to the reins, but Lydia fell. The next thing she knew she was spread out on the hard ground, and her ankle throbbed with pain.

Kaikai was kneeling over her. "Are you all right?" she cried.

"M—my foot hurts." Lydia's lips trembled.

Kaikai rubbed her fingers gently over the sore ankle. "It is not broken," she said. "Just the

74

same, I think you and I had better go back to the village. We mustn't take a chance."

"Oh, Kaikai, please! I want to see the volcano," Lydia wailed. "My ankle doesn't hurt much. Honestly it doesn't."

Just then the King galloped up on his big white horse. "Lydia had a fall?" he said. He climbed down and examined her ankle. "No, it is not broken, but it might be sprained. You cannot ride horseback."

Lydia's chin quivered. The King was going to send her back to the village. She wouldn't get to see the volcano after all!

The King pulled a big white handkerchief from his pocket and wrapped it around the throbbing ankle. Then he clapped his hands together for one of his servants.

He whispered something in the servant's ear. "He must be telling him to take me back," Lydia thought. She blinked to hold back the tears.

75

The King lifted her gently in his arms. He carried her past Kaikai's horse and Bernice's horse to a donkey cart. The servant pushed aside the supplies in the cart and spread out a sleeping mat in the bottom.

Carefully, the King set Lydia down. "There, now," he said. "You can ride up to the crater in comfort!" He waved his arm. The party moved on toward the volcano.

The Earth's Fireworks

ALL AFTERNOON Lydia jogged along in the donkey cart. The party left the jungle and finally drew near the edge of the volcano.

Lydia looked out over the black land. It was covered with hundreds of queer-shaped rocks. There were no flowers or green things. Nothing grew but a few red berries. "It's much colder up here," Lydia thought, slipping on a sweater.

The party stopped. Victoria and Kaikai came over to the cart. "How is your foot, Lydia?" Kaikai asked, helping her out.

Lydia set one foot on the ground, then the other. "It doesn't hurt any more!" she cried.

"Good!" Kaikai said. "That means it wasn't sprained after all."

Lydia sniffed. "What's that funny smell?"

Victoria giggled. "It smells like eggs that have been left in the sun too long. Look!" She pointed toward a spurt of steam shooting up through a crack in the ground.

"You smell sulfur from deep in the earth," Kaikai explained. "It smells like that because it is warm. Come, the King has told everyone to dismount. The path is narrow, and we must walk the rest of the way on foot. It is not far. The servants will take care of the horses."

Lydia and Victoria followed Kaikai's tall figure. They had been traveling uphill all day. Now the path seemed to be going downward. In some places, the ground felt hot underfoot, and broken bits of hardened lava tore at the soles of their shoes.

"It's spooky up here!" Victoria said.

They walked carefully, past two huts made of tree boughs. Then they caught up with the King. He was waiting by the edge of a great hole in the earth. He pointed downward. "This is Kilauea," he said in his deep voice.

Lydia held her breath and looked into the pit. "It must be a million feet deep!" she thought. Still, she was a little disappointed. She had expected to see bright fires, but all she could see were big puffs of mist floating about in the crater.

"Don't worry," said the King. "When the mist has cleared and darkness comes, the volcano will look different. Then you will see the most brilliant fireworks you can imagine!"

"I can see a little fire over there, where there is no mist," Lydia said, "but it isn't bright."

"That is because it is still day."

Suddenly a thick mass of gray mud rose up through the mist, rolling over and over.

"It looks like big snakes!" cried Victoria.

Kaikai laughed. "These are the only snakes you will find in all our islands." She reached into a basket she was carrying and took out two bananas. "Throw these into the pit," she said, handing them to Lydia and Victoria. "They are your offering to Pele, the goddess of the volcano."

"Pele!" Lydia cried. "Papa Paki taught me a song about her once. Let's throw the bananas at the same time, Victoria. Ready? Set! Go!" The girls tossed the bananas into the pit.

There was a gulping sound, and a puff of steam. The gray mud wriggled and bubbled. The bananas disappeared.

"Pele must have liked them, she ate them so fast," Lydia cried.

The King laughed. "We shall eat now ourselves," he said. He pointed toward the two shelters, set well back from the edge of the crater.

"Good! We're hungry."

Everyone went into one of the huts and sat on the earth floor. The servants spread grass mats on the ground and set heaping wooden platters of meat and chicken on the mats.

Lydia looked around. The hut had a roof and sides, but no front. "Are we going to sleep in here, too?" she asked.

"Yes," Kaikai said. "You children and I will use this shelter. The grownups will use the other."

"Then we can watch the volcano before we go to sleep," Lydia thought.

81

The King passed her the bowl of poi. "Did you bring your guitar, Lydia? Will you sing us a song after you have eaten?"

Lydia blushed. "Yes, my guitar is in the supply cart, Your Majesty."

"I will have one of my servants get it."

"What shall I sing?" Lydia said. "I know! The old song Papa Paki taught me about Pele!"

When she had finished eating, the King's servant handed her the guitar. She stood up and strummed a few notes. Then, in Hawaiian, she chanted,

"Pele, Pele, Goddess of fire,
It is you we all admire.
Be good to our people,
Be good to us all,
Show us your fires. Hear our call!"

Everyone clapped. "You have a sweet voice," the King said, smiling with pleasure. "I'm glad you're making good use of the guitar I gave you."

Suddenly, Kaikai pointed toward the crater. "There is the fire!" she cried.

Everyone looked out of the hut and down at the pit.

"How different it looks against the darkness!" Lydia cried.

The King motioned them out of the shelter. "Stay well back from the edge," he said, "and there will be no danger."

They looked down. Red fountains of flame leaped into the air. Waves of fire rolled round and round the pit.

Lydia pointed to a great mass of black lava on the far side of the pit. It bubbled and boiled, throwing orange sparks in every direction.

Kaikai handed each of the girls a cloth bag with two holes cut in it. "Put them on, so your faces won't be burned," she said, loudly enough to be heard above the crackle of flames. "Even here, the fires are hot."

They covered their faces with the masks. "Now it's really spooky!" Lydia cried. "We all look like ghosts."

She and Victoria clung to each other and stared down at the flames, which made ever-changing pictures against the darkness.

"Look!" Lydia cried. "Doesn't that look like a face? Maybe that's the goddess Pele."

Finally, Kaikai took them by the hand. "Come. It is time for you to settle down for the night."

They went into the shelter and lay down on the mats. Lydia and Victoria turned over on their stomachs to watch the volcano.

"I was reminded of your great-aunt when you sang tonight, Lydia," Kaikai said.

"You mean the one Papa Paki told me about? The one who was Queen?"

"Yes. She lived many years ago. She was one of the greatest queens Hawaii ever had, and she performed her greatest deed right here."

"What was it? Tell us," Victoria said.

Kaikai sat down. "This Queen was one of the first women to be taught by the missionaries," she said. "One day, a missionary-teacher came to the Queen's home in Honolulu. The teacher said that some of the people on the island of Hawaii would not give up their old ways.

" 'They still believe in the goddess of the volcano,' the missionary-teacher said to the Queen. 'Some of these people are very poor. Even so, they throw great amounts of food into the crater for the goddess.'

" 'That is bad,' the Queen told the teacher. 'My people need their food. I shall go to the big island myself.'

"She and her royal party came to Hawaii and traveled all the way up here."

"Just as we did!" Lydia interrupted.

"Yes, and many of the people who lived on the island followed her. When they came near the

86

crater, the Queen cried out to them, 'Watch me, my people!' She ran about, picking the little red berries that grew at the edge of the crater.

" 'Stop!' the people cried. 'You must not pick those berries. They belong to Pele. She will harm you!'

"The Queen kept on picking the berries. 'I will show you that Pele has no power,' she said. She ran back and forth to the edge of the crater. She ate some of the berries. She threw some into the burning pit. All the while, she sang the hymns the missionary-teachers had taught her.

" 'Now!' she cried. 'If there really is a goddess in that volcano, she will destroy me.'

"The people gasped. They were afraid for their Queen, but the fires of the volcano stayed within the pit, just as they did tonight.

" 'You see,' the Queen cried. 'There is no Pele! You must not throw all your food into the crater for her.'

"After that, the people believed their missionary-teachers. They knew that there really was no volcano goddess."

"Why did we throw in the bananas?" Lydia asked, puzzled.

"Just for fun, and to remember the ways of long ago," Kaikai told her.

Lydia gazed at the fire in the crater. "My great-aunt was a good, brave queen," she said. "She really loved her people. If I were a queen, I would try to be like her."

Opening Night
at the Theater

ONE DAY Lydia and Bernice were walking down King Street in Honolulu. This was 1847, and many of the grass houses had disappeared from the center of the city. Lydia looked up at the new brick buildings that had taken their places. There was a sign on one of them. It read:

FIRST THEATER IN HAWAII
OPENING SATURDAY NIGHT

"I'd love to go!" Lydia cried.

"I don't think Mrs. Cooke will let you," Bernice said. "She doesn't like the theater."

"There will be music and singing," Lydia went

on. "How I'd like to go! I know what I'll do. I'll ask the King! If he says I should go, maybe Mrs. Cooke will let me."

On the way back to school, Lydia made Bernice stop at the King's palace. It was not really a palace, but a large American-style house with a porch all around it. It had been built just the year before.

A guard in a blue uniform and a tall white hat marched back and forth on the porch.

Lydia walked up the steps and stood in front of the guard. "I want to see the King," she said.

Bernice stood at the bottom of the steps, her mouth open in amazement.

The guard stopped marching. "The King is busy, little girl. You'd better run along."

"This is important!" Lydia stood straight and threw back her shoulders. "Tell him Lydia, Chief Paki's daughter, is here."

The guard clicked his boots and went inside.

Bernice came running up the steps and tugged at Lydia's arm. "How can you be so—so bold?" she cried. "Come on, let's go."

"No," Lydia said firmly. "I want to go to the theater Saturday."

The guard returned. "The King will see you," he said with a bow.

The King was sitting behind a big desk. It was piled high with papers. He looked up as Lydia entered the room. "Good morning, Lydia. I understand you have important business to see me about this morning."

Now Lydia felt shy. Bernice was right. This *was* a bold thing to do! The King was so busy. "It—it's about the theater, Your Majesty." She spoke quickly, as if to get it over with.

The King looked bewildered. "If you wish to go to the theater, why don't you ask Mrs. Cooke?"

"I—I don't think she'll let me go. I thought maybe if you spoke to her——"

"Mrs. Cooke doesn't approve of the theater, Your Majesty," Bernice interrupted.

"I see." Now the King put down his long, feathered pen and leaned back in his chair. "I do not like to interfere with Mrs. Cooke's rules. Still, it must be important to you, Lydia, or you would not have come to see me. Why? Why is it so important that you go to the theater?"

"I'd like to hear the music, Your Majesty, and I'd like to see the actors in their fine costumes. I've read about the theaters in England and the United States. All the grand ladies and gentlemen go."

The King smiled. "Starting a theater in Hawaii does show how much our country is learning about modern ways," he said. "Perhaps it would be a good thing if you did go." He reached in his desk drawer and pulled out a blank sheet of paper. "How about you, Bernice? Is it as important to you as it is to your sister?"

92

Bernice hesitated. "I would like to go," she said, "but not so much as Lydia. These things mean more to her than they do to me."

The King dipped his pen in an inkwell and wrote something on the paper. He folded the paper and placed it inside an envelope. "Give this to Mrs. Cooke," he said.

"Thank you, Your Majesty! Thank you!"

When Mrs. Cooke ripped open the envelope

and read the paper inside, her eyes opened wide with surprise. "Do you mean you went to see the King about this, Lydia?" she asked. "Land sakes, why would you do such a thing? You hadn't even asked me about it."

"I—I didn't think you would let me go," Lydia said. "I want to go so badly, too! The King says the opening of the theater shows how much Hawaii is learning about modern ways."

"Yes," Mrs. Cooke said slowly, "I suppose that is true." She put her hands on Lydia's shoulders. "When you make up your mind to do something, you remind me of your ancestors, the Hawaiian chiefs of old."

"You mean the first people who came to Hawaii, the ones who traveled thousands of miles across the ocean in canoes?" asked Lydia.

"That's right. They wouldn't give up, and when you want something, you won't either. I shall ask Kaikai to go with you."

"I'll wear my new dress," Lydia said. "I'll pile my hair up on my head!"

"No," Mrs. Cooke said firmly. "You are too young for that."

"Oh, Mrs. Cooke, please——"

"Come now, Lydia. Is pinning your hair up so important? Is it important enough to be stubborn about?" Mrs. Cooke asked.

"No," Lydia said quietly. "I'll wear my hair down if you say I must."

Saturday night came at last, and Lydia and Kaikai went to the theater. They sat in a box reserved especially for ladies. Lydia looked around. She noticed that there were no cushions on the unreserved seats in the back of the theater. Her own seat had a nice soft cushion.

"There's the King," she whispered to Kaikai. She nodded toward the next box. "It looks more grown-up to nod than to wave," she thought.

The King sat with the Queen and some of his

advisers from the United States. He smiled and nodded back at Lydia.

The stage was made of rough wood. There was no curtain. The musicians in front of the stage were all dressed in American clothes.

Excitement rippled through the audience as the music started. The Hawaiian people had no national anthem, so everyone stood up and sang, "God Save the King." It was the British national anthem, and it had the same tune as "America."

Lydia sang along with the others. As she sang, she thought, "The Hawaiian people should not have to sing someone else's national anthem. They should have an anthem of their own."

When the anthem was finished, the people in the theater sat down. An actor came out on the stage and held up a big card. On the card was printed the name of the play, *The Adopted Child*. The lamps were dimmed and the play began.

Lydia was delighted. She felt as if she had

suddenly been carried off to another world. All the actors were men. Even the "ladies" were men dressed in women's clothes, but they seemed very real to Lydia.

When the show was over, the orchestra played a few Hawaiian melodies and the audience sang. Lydia joined in the singing happily.

Afterward Kaikai took Lydia back to school.

"You know, Kaikai," Lydia said on the way, "I wish we had our own national anthem to sing."

Kaikai smiled. "You like to make up songs. Why don't you write one?"

"I'm serious," Lydia said, shaking her head. "We ought to have one."

"Well, maybe some day we will."

Captain Cook's Discovery

LYDIA LOVED to read. One day she was curled up in her room with a history book. Turning a page, she came upon a picture of a tall, fair man in white breeches, a three-cornered hat, and buckled shoes.

"Captain James Cook, discoverer of the Hawaiian Islands," she read.

Lydia ran down to the classroom. None of the other children was there, but Mrs. Cooke sat at her desk, correcting some papers.

"Was Captain Cook your father?" Lydia asked, holding up the picture so that Mrs. Cooke could see it.

The teacher laughed. "Land sakes, no! He just happened to have the same name. See?" She pointed to the printing under the picture. "His name has no *e* on the end of it."

"Oh! Well, who was he, anyway? It says here that he discovered Hawaii!"

Mrs. Cooke put down her pencil. "Yes, he was the first white man ever to come here." She laughed a little. "In fact, Lydia, even though he wasn't related to me, I guess I wouldn't be here now if it weren't for him."

"Why? Did he bring you?"

"Heavens, no, child. He came here in 1778. That was seventy years ago. I've only been here ten years. I just meant that people in other parts of the world didn't even know the Hawaiian Islands were here in the Pacific Ocean until Captain Cook discovered them.

"He sailed all the way from England. The Hawaiians had never seen such a big ship before.

When it sailed into the bay, the people on shore thought it was an island floating in the sea."

Lydia giggled.

"When Captain Cook landed, everyone crowded around and stared at him. 'Look!' they said, as he reached into his pockets, 'he has openings in the sides of his body!'

"The Hawaiians prepared a big feast and treated him like a king. When he returned to the islands a few months later, however, he was killed in a fight. His men took the maps he had drawn back to England, and that is how the people of the world learned about Hawaii.

"Before long, many trading ships and big whaling ships came. There are many whalers in New England, you know, and they found Hawaii a good stopping-off place."

"They still do!" Lydia piped up. "I see them in the harbor all the time. How did you happen to come here?"

"Well, that brings me to another part of the story. There was a Hawaiian lad by the name of Henry Obookiah. Henry was very eager to learn how to read and write. Of course, there were no schools or teachers here in those days, so Henry went to the United States on a whaling ship.

"When the ship landed, he went to Yale University, a school in the state of Connecticut. He sat on the steps and waited until some of the students came out. Then he jumped up. 'Please, will you teach me to read?' he cried.

"The students did. Henry told them about his people in Hawaii. 'I must learn all I can,' he said. 'Then I will go back and teach them.' "

"Did he?" Lydia asked eagerly.

"No. Henry fell ill and died, but his American friends took his place. They formed a group of missionaries, and in 1820 they came to Hawaii."

"Were you with them?"

"No. I came with another group eighteen

years later." Mrs. Cooke chuckled. "How strange those first missionaries must have looked to the Hawaiians, Lydia. Their clothes must have looked just as strange to the Hawaiians as the Hawaiians' clothes looked to them."

"The Hawaiians wore a cloth wrapped around them, just as I do today when I'm not in school." Lydia grew thoughtful. "Mrs. Cooke, do the Hawaiians still seem strange to you?"

The teacher pushed her glasses up on her nose and smiled. "Some of your ways are different from ours, but you are learning quickly," she said. She came over and put her hand on Lydia's shoulder. "I guess we make a good combination," she went on. "We teach you to read, and you teach us to laugh."

Lydia Helps Out

LYDIA WAS nine. One night at school, she was sound asleep when she felt someone shaking her bed. Opening her eyes, she could barely see Victoria's long nightdress in the moonlight streaming in through the window.

"My head hurts," Victoria said weakly. She started to cough. "I feel awful."

Now Lydia was wide awake. She jumped up. "Go back to bed. I'll get Mrs. Cooke." She pulled the covers up over Victoria's shoulders. Then she felt her way down to the teacher's room.

"Mrs. Cooke!" she called. "Come quick! Victoria's sick!"

103

When they got back upstairs, Mrs. Cooke put her hand on Victoria's forehead. "What is the matter, dear?" she asked.

"My head hurts, and I'm cold." Victoria shivered, even under the warm covers.

"You don't seem to have any fever," said Mrs. Cooke. "Try to go back to sleep. If you're not better in the morning, I'll send for the doctor. Lydia, you had better sleep in Bernice's room. Victoria may have something catching."

"Please," Lydia cried. "Let me stay here. She might want something."

"Well, all right. You've been with her up till now, so I suppose you'll be all right. You'd better go back to bed now, though."

Lydia could not fall asleep. She was worried. She had heard that many people in Hawaii had the measles now. The Hawaiian people were healthy because they spent so much time outdoors, but many could not get over measles.

Victoria tossed and turned all night long. Every once in a while Lydia got up and put her hand on her friend's forehead, as Mrs. Cooke had done. By morning, Victoria felt hot. Lydia dipped a cloth into a bowl of water on the dresser. Just as she was placing it on Victoria's head, Mrs. Cooke came in.

The teacher bent over and looked at Victoria's face. "How do you feel this morning, dear?" she asked softly.

Victoria opened her eyes. They were red.

"I'm hot," she said, "and my eyes hurt."

Mrs. Cooke turned to Lydia. "Go down and tell one of the boys to go for the doctor."

When the doctor came, he sent Lydia out of the room. She waited outside in the hall. She heard him tapping Victoria's chest and thumping her back. Then he said, "Open your mouth wide, please, young lady."

Lydia knew that he was using a flat stick to

hold Victoria's tongue down so he could look at her throat. There was a long silence. Finally the doctor spoke. "It must be the measles," he said.

Lydia gasped. Poor Victoria!

"All the children must stay here at school," the doctor said. "They cannot leave the grounds for any reason."

"Not even to go to church?"

"No, not even for that." The doctor walked to the window and pulled down the shade. "Keep it dark in here, so that her eyes won't hurt," he said firmly.

Lydia sat outside the bedroom door all morning. She strummed her guitar and sang funny songs, hoping to make Victoria laugh.

Mrs. Cooke kept coming upstairs to care for the sick girl. At last she came up with a tray.

"I can take that," Lydia said.

"No, dear. We wouldn't want you to get sick, too," Mrs. Cooke said.

At that moment Bernice called from downstairs. "Mrs. Cooke! Come quick! Alexander doesn't feel very well."

"My land, he must have the measles, too! I guess you'll have to take this, Lydia," Mrs. Cooke said, handing Lydia the tray.

Lydia walked tall and straight as she carried the tray in to Victoria. "I've brought you some nice tea," she said, just as she had heard Mrs. Cooke say. "Have some!"

"I don't feel like it."

"It will help you get better." Lydia set the tray on the bedside table and pulled a big pillow off the shelf in the closet. The Hawaiian people never slept with pillows, but Mrs. Cooke had brought some from the United States. Lydia placed the pillow behind Victoria's back so that she could sit up in bed. Even though the shade was drawn, Lydia could see red blotches beginning to break out on her friend's face.

"If I could make her laugh, maybe she would drink the tea," Lydia thought.

"Victoria's covered with millions of dots.
They look just like a leopard's spots!"

Victoria giggled and drank her tea.

That night, however, she was worse. She had a high fever. She thrashed about in bed, threw off her covers, and cried out in her sleep.

Lydia got up and held her friend's warm hand. She pulled the covers back up over her shoulders. Still Victoria was restless.

"Maybe she'd feel better if she could see a grownup in her own family," Lydia whispered when Mrs. Cooke came into the room. "Can her father come to school?"

"No," the teacher said as she set her lamp on the dresser. "Her father has never had the measles. It wouldn't be safe for him to come."

Lydia looked down at Victoria. In the dimly-lighted room, Victoria looked thin and wan.

"Who else would come?" Lydia thought. She knew that Victoria's mother had died when Victoria was just a small baby.

"I know!" she whispered. "Her aunt lives on the other side of a big garden, just back of the goat's yard. Maybe she has had the measles."

"I'll go and see," Mrs. Cooke said.

"Go through the goat's yard," Lydia suggested. "It's much faster."

A few minutes later, Victoria's aunt came hurrying into the room. She smiled quickly at Lydia. Then she sat down next to the sick girl.

"There, there, dear," she said softly, stroking Victoria's hair back from her face. "See what I have brought you!" She lifted something out of a basket. It was a kitten!

"Let's call her Measles!" Lydia cried.

Victoria's eyes fluttered open. She smiled. "Thank you, Aunty. Thank you." She dropped off to sleep with her hand on the kitten's neck.

110

For the rest of the night, Victoria slept quietly. In a few days, she felt better.

Alexander did have the measles. David caught them, too. Mrs. Cooke put them together in the room across the hall.

Two weeks passed. Lydia worked hard. She helped Mrs. Cooke carry trays, and she amused the patients. She did not catch the measles.

At last everyone began to grow better. One day Lydia was reading to Victoria. The kitten was asleep at the foot of the bed. Suddenly, a big pillow came sailing across the room. Plop! It landed in Lydia's lap.

"It must be Alexander and David!" Victoria cried, sitting up.

Lydia took the pillow. She ran out to the hall and peeked into the boys' room. Everything was quiet. The boys were in bed, with the covers drawn up to their chins. They were pretending to be asleep.

There was a muffled laugh from David's bed. Lydia lifted the pillow high over her head and hurled it at David, but she threw it too hard. The seams ripped open, and goose feathers flew everywhere.

The boys sat up. They sneezed and laughed at the same time.

Victoria came running in with another pillow. She tossed it at Alexander. More sneezing! More laughing and shouting!

Suddenly, David clapped his hand over his mouth. Mrs. Cooke was standing in the doorway. She sneezed, too.

"I'm glad you're all feeling better," she said with a smile. "As for you, Lydia, you deserve a bit of fun. You have been a good nurse's helper." She picked up a pillow and tossed it to her.

The Little Men

It was vacation time again. Lydia, Victoria, David, and Bernice had come to the island of Kauai. They were on a beach with Kaikai.

"This is a famous beach," Kaikai said, sitting down on the sand.

"What's the name of it?" Lydia asked. She leaned over to pat Measles, the cat, who had come along with them.

"I will not tell you until later," Kaikai answered mysteriously. She pointed to some hills of sand almost fifty feet high. "Look at those dunes over there. Before you go for a swim, why don't you run up and slide down them?"

Lydia leaned over and picked up Measles. "Come on, Measles, I'll give you a ride." She scrambled to the top of the dune. The others ran up the dune after her.

"Let's all go down together!" David cried. "Sit down and slide!"

Lydia's arm tightened around the cat. She gave herself a push with her free hand. Down she went!

"Yip! Yip!" There was a barking sound somewhere behind her.

Lydia glanced back. There must be a dog somewhere near by, but where was it? She couldn't see anything. She slid faster and faster. Now the yipping turned to howling. Measles squirmed in Lydia's arms.

Everyone slid to the bottom of the sand-hill. The howling stopped. Where was the dog? The children looked up to the top of the dunes. They could see nothing but sand and a few swaying palm trees.

"You stay here with Measles," Victoria cried. "I'll go see whether the dog is behind one of those palm trees up there."

She came back shaking her head.

Kaikai came toward them.

"We heard a dog howl!" Lydia cried. "He scared Measles, but we can't find him!"

The nursemaid's shoulders shook with laughter. "That is why I would not tell you the name of this beach," she said. "It is called 'Beach of the Barking Sands.' There is no dog. It's a special kind of sand that makes noise when you slide on it. It's part coral and part lava."

Lydia laughed. "I'll take some home to show Mrs. Cooke. We'd better not slide any more, though. Measles still thinks it was a real dog."

David had already started up the dune. The sand howled as he came sliding down. The cat jumped out of Lydia's arms and ran back and forth. "Meow! Meow!" she cried.

"That's enough, David," Kaikai called to him. "Later, perhaps, we will go leaf-sliding on the hillside behind the beach."

Lydia and Victoria caught the cat. They patted her until she had stopped trembling. Then they gave her to Kaikai while they went bathing in the ocean.

Lydia swam through the water with smooth, even strokes. She had learned to swim almost as soon as she had learned to walk. She swam down-shore, until she reached a row of rocks that jutted far out into the ocean. "They look like a long, bony finger," she thought.

She turned around and swam back. Then she ran up to Kaikai on the sand. "What's that row of rocks in the water?" she asked.

"That is one of the breakwaters built by the Little Men."

"Papa Paki told me something about the Little Men once," Lydia said as she lay down on the sand. "They were the ones who used to do wonderful things at night."

Kaikai nodded. "Long ago," she said, "thousands of Little Men were supposed to have lived here on our island. Would you like to hear more about them, Lydia?"

Everyone gathered around to listen.

"Some people say the Little Men were like fairies," she said. "Others believe they were real people, only two or three feet high."

117

"I'm taller than that!" Lydia said.

"Yes, you all are. The Little Men did many kinds of work. They built bridges and dams and breakwaters, like the one out there in the water. They worked very fast, and they did all their work at night."

"Couldn't they see in the daytime?" Victoria wanted to know.

"Yes, they could see. They just believed that they would turn to stone if the sun came up while they were working."

"Did anyone ever see these Little Men?" asked Lydia curiously.

"No. Human beings could not see them, but people used to hear their voices ring through the forest. Since no one could see them, it was easy for the Little Men to play jokes on people."

"What kind of jokes?"

"Well, there is an old story of a boy named Laka. Now Laka lived many years ago. He was

118

always asking his father for new playthings. No sooner would his father bring them, than Laka would ask for more. Finally there were no playthings on his island that Laka didn't have. So his father set out in his canoe for another island. 'I will find you new ones, my son,' he said.

"Months went by, but Laka's father did not come back.

" 'What do you think happened to him?' Laka asked his grandmother.

" 'He is probably shipwrecked on some lonely beach,' she answered. 'You must build a canoe and go find him.'

"Laka took his ax and climbed into the mountains. He searched until he found a tall, straight tree. 'This will make a fine canoe,' he said to himself. He chopped away at the tree all day long. By evening, the tree had fallen to the ground, but Laka was too tired to build his canoe. 'I shall hollow it out in the morning,' he thought. He lay down on the ground and fell asleep. When he awoke——"

"His canoe was already built!" Lydia cried.

"No, you are wrong," Kaikai laughed. "It was just the opposite. The tree stood upright again, as if it had not been chopped down at all!

" 'How could this happen?' Laka thought. He looked all about, but he saw no one. He stood still and listened. Above the sounds of the forest, he heard the humming of voices. The voices seemed to laugh and fade away.

"Laka called out. He ran about, trying to find where the voices came from, but he could find no one.

" 'I shall chop the tree down again,' he thought. He chopped and chopped, until by evening the tree lay on the ground. Then Laka fell asleep.

"The next morning, the tree stood upright again! Once more Laka chopped it down. That evening he thought, 'Tonight I shall not lie down and sleep. I shall stay awake and see who has been doing this.'

"He hid in the hollow of another tree. He watched and waited. Nothing happened until it had grown dark. Then, all at once, Laka heard the humming of voices again. They grew louder and louder, but he could see no one.

"Then he heard a high, squeaky voice. 'Hah!' the voice said. 'He has chopped the tree down again. We must put it together at once!'

"Laka heard laughing and chattering and the rustling of leaves. It sounded as if the leaves were being glued back onto the branches of the tree that he had cut down. Finally he heard the tree trunk move across the ground, as if it were being pushed.

"Laka rushed out of his hiding place. Even though the moon shone brightly, he could see no one. He reached out. He felt many little people and grasped two of them by the arms.

" 'Let us go!' they cried.

" 'Why do you keep putting my tree back where it was?' Laka asked.

" 'Because this is our forest! The tree is ours. It belongs here, not bobbing up and down in the ocean somewhere!'

" 'My father sailed to another island. He has not come back,' Laka said. 'I must build a canoe so that I can go to find him. Why do you do this to me?' Laka let go of the Little Men and started to cry. 'I must find my father,' he sobbed.

"When he finally stopped crying, he heard the Little Men whispering among themselves. Then one of them spoke.

" 'We will help you,' he said. 'We did not know why you needed the canoe. Go to sleep now. When you wake up, you shall see how good the Little Men can be.'

"Laka lay down on the ground and went to sleep. When he awoke, he saw before him a

122

beautiful canoe, all ready to be carried down to
the water.

"'Oh, thank you! You are good!' he cried. He
lifted the canoe to his shoulders and carried it
down to the ocean and sailed away."

"Did he find his father?" Lydia asked.

"Yes, he sailed to the island of Hawaii and found his father on a deserted reef."

"I'll bet he never asked for new toys again!" Lydia said. Then she asked, "Do you believe there really were Little Men, Kaikai?"

"Well, the Hawaiian people have always kept a careful record of everything they ever built," Kaikai said with a smile. "However, there is no record of the building of that breakwater, or of many of the bridges and walls you can find in the islands. Who knows? Someone must have built those things."

Fishing Festival

WHEN THE King came to the beach that afternoon he brought his surfboards with him. He and the boys skimmed high over the rolling waves. Sometimes they lay flat on the boards. Sometimes they stood up. Once David even rode standing on his head.

"It looks like so much fun!" Lydia cried. "I'm going to try it!" She ran down to the water.

"Don't you stand on your head!" Kaikai called.

Lydia waited until David rode up to shore. "Will you give me a ride?" she called out.

"All right," he said, "but you'll have to help me paddle."

She ran into the water and lay down flat on the board. David knelt behind her. They put out their arms until their hands hung down on either side. They made the board move by paddling with their hands.

Soon they passed the spot where the waves broke. David turned the board around until it pointed toward shore. He looked back over his shoulder. "We'll wait for just the right wave," he said.

Lydia felt the board rise up under her. It was as if a giant under the ocean were lifting her into the air. She held her breath as the board sped toward shore.

Suddenly, a cross wave splashed over the board. Almost before Lydia knew what was happening, the board flipped over. Water rushed over her head. She kicked her feet and waved her arms. Finally she rose to the surface.

"Are you all right?" David shouted.

"Just wet!" she laughed.

David pointed toward the surfboard. It was racing ahead without them! They swam after it with long, sure strokes. David held the board steady while Lydia climbed on again. Then they waited for another wave. This time, the wave carried them all the way to shore.

Lydia scrambled to her feet. "That was fun!" she said breathlessly. "Next time, though, I'll ride by myself." She ran over to where Kaikai sat with Victoria.

"You ought to try it," she said to Victoria.

"I'd be too scared."

"How about you, Kaikai?"

"We're not all as brave as you are, Lydia. Besides, I'm so fat there's not a wave in the ocean big enough to lift me." Kaikai laughed. Then she added seriously, "Lie down and rest a minute. You don't want to grow too tired."

Lydia lay back on the sand.

"We're lucky to live in Hawaii where it's warm all the time," she said. "Mrs. Cooke told us that where she comes from, people can swim only in the summer."

"That must be awful," Victoria agreed. She pointed to the path that ran along the beach. Many carts were coming along the path. They were filled with people. "Who are all those people?" she asked.

"They are from the village," Kaikai said. "They are having a fishing festival."

"Oh, good! We've never seen one."

Now the people were getting out of the carts. Some of the men carried a huge net.

"What are those leaves hanging from the net?" Lydia asked, jumping to her feet.

"When the sun shines on the leaves, they cast shadows on the water," Kaikai explained. "The fishermen think the shadows frighten the fish so that they swim into the net."

128

The King and the boys came out of the surf. Everyone watched the fishermen. There were ropes fastened to the corners of their net. They tied the ropes around a tree. Then they swam far out into the ocean with the net.

Suddenly one of the fishermen yelled.

"There must be a shark out there!" Victoria cried in alarm.

The King laughed. "No. They make that noise to frighten the fish into the net!"

The men left the net in the water and swam back to shore.

"They will leave it there for two hours," the King said. "Then we will all help to pull it in. It is an old Hawaiian custom that anyone who helps pull in the net gets a share of the catch."

Now the fishermen ran over to the carts and started to unload baskets of food.

Before long, all the people of the village were working to prepare for the feast. While the men

carried things, two women were arranging mel-
ons and bananas on big leaves. Others were
plucking feathers from chickens. All the while,
everyone sang beautiful Hawaiian songs.

Lydia and Victoria saw two boys scamper up
a tall palm tree.

"Watch out!" the boys called from the top.

The girls jumped out of the way.

Plop! The boys threw coconuts to the ground.
Then they slid back down the trunks of the trees.

They opened the coconuts by cracking them against big rocks, and poured the milk into a bowl. Then they pried out chunks of white coconut meat and rubbed them over a grater. The grater was made of nails hammered into a block of wood.

Lydia's mouth watered as she watched the shredded coconut pile up in a big wooden bowl under the grater.

Just then, Kaikai came over and handed each of the girls a banana.

"The feast will not be ready for a while," she said. "In the meantime, would you like to go leaf-sliding? There is a slippery hill not far from the beach."

"I hope it doesn't bark like the sand dunes," Lydia said. "Measles has had enough of that."

Kaikai laughed. "No, but just the same, I think we had better leave Measles here with one of the village women."

The royal children piled into a donkey cart. They rode until they came to a smooth, damp hillside with very little grass on it.

Lydia and Victoria ran about and gathered some big shiny leaves. Then they scrambled to the top of the hill. They sat down on the leaves and held the stalks in both hands. They gave themselves a push. The bottom of the hill seemed to rush up toward them. What fun it was! They laughed so hard, they could not stop!

When they got to the bottom, they climbed back up the slope and slid down again. Now all the children were sliding. The slope became muddier. Before long everyone was covered with mud.

"You'll have to wash yourselves in the ocean," Kaikai told them. "We'd better go back to the beach now, anyway. It's almost time to pull in the fishing net. Don't forget to plant your leaves before we go."

132

The children poked the stalks into the soft wet ground and pressed dirt around them.

"Good!" Kaikai said. "Now they will grow again. Everything grows in Hawaii."

The sun was setting when they returned to the beach. It looked like a huge orange resting on the water. Suddenly it disappeared behind the rolling water, and only red and yellow streamers were left in the sky.

The children ran into the water and washed off the mud. When they came out, the village people and the King were standing near the ropes which held the net in the ocean.

"Come, children," the King called. "You can help pull in the net."

Lydia and Victoria squeezed in among the others. The rope felt slippery under Lydia's wet hand, but she held on tight.

"When I count to three, pull," the King said. "One! Two! Three! *Pull!*"

Everyone tugged. As they pulled the net into the shore, the fishermen sang.

> "Fish of our sea,
> Food of our land,
> Swim to our net,
> Come to our sand!"

The children crowded around the net. It was filled with hundreds of fish. How they shone as they flopped up and down!

"It is a good catch," the King said.

Someone blew into a big seashell.

"That means that they are ready to take the roast pigs out of the pit," Kaikai said. "They have been roasting there for hours."

The children gathered around the pit. It was covered with leaves and sand. An old man knelt beside it.

"He is the oldest man in the village," Kaikai whispered. "He has been given the honor of opening the pit."

134

Everyone was quiet as the old man scraped away the top layer of sand. Then he began to lift off the leaves.

The crowd moved closer. They looked down into the pit. Two big roast pigs sizzled in their juices. How brown and crispy they were!

"How good they smell!" thought Lydia.

Now the village people spread out the food on the sand where everyone was to eat. Wooden platters overflowed with all kinds of food. There were plump chickens cooked in coconut milk, and sweet shrimp from the sea. There were long ears of golden corn, fragrant baked bananas, dark red yams, and great bowls of lavender poi.

Victoria smacked her lips. "It all looks so good, I don't know what to eat first!"

Lydia dipped her fingers into the bowl of poi With a quick twist of the wrist, she popped the pasty mixture into her mouth. Then she passed the bowl to Victoria.

The feast lasted for many hours. When it was finished, Lydia played her guitar, while some girls from the village danced the hula. The leaf skirts of the dancers swayed to the strains of the young girl's music. The movements of their graceful hands told the story of the dance. Lydia sang the words of the story.

When the dancers waved their hands over their heads, Lydia sang, "The sky."

The dancers drew a circle in the air.

Lydia sang, "The sun."

The dancers fluttered their hands gracefully from side to side.

"The waves on the shore," Lydia sang in clear, sweet tones. "This is our Hawaii."

Christmas at
School

It was the day before Christmas. Lydia was in the kitchen of the Royal Boarding School, helping Mrs. Cooke crack some nuts to put in a special holiday pudding.

The teacher sighed. "Christmas isn't the same here as it is in New England," she said, more to herself than to Lydia.

"Why?" Lydia piped up. "We always go to church and sing the carols you taught us."

"I know." Mrs. Cooke handed her a bowl for the nut shells. "I miss the Christmas trees we used to have. They were so pretty when they were trimmed with colored ornaments and popcorn strings and a star at the top. I would like to see some snow, too."

"It never gets cold enough to snow here, except on the highest mountains," Lydia said thoughtfully, "but why can't we have a Christmas tree?"

Mrs. Cooke laughed. "Hawaiian soil is fertile, but it doesn't grow pine trees," she said.

Lydia finished cracking the nuts. Then she hurried out to the courtyard and told the other children what Mrs. Cooke had said. They looked at one another in silence.

All at once, Lydia's eyes sparkled. "I have an idea," she cried. "Let's surprise Mrs. Cooke. Let's make this Christmas like the ones she used to have at home!"

"How?" Victoria asked.

Lydia pointed to a low palm tree growing next to the wall in the courtyard.

"Why can't we use that for a Christmas tree?"

"It doesn't look like a pine tree," Victoria said. "Pine trees are tall." She raised her arms way over her head. "They have stiff branches and they come to a point on top."

"I know, silly, but we could decorate it."

"Where would we get the decorations?" Bernice asked. "We don't have any colored balls or popcorn to string."

"We'll use flowers," Lydia said. "We'll string shells. I have lots of shells. It will be a Hawaiian Christmas tree!"

David jumped to his feet. "I'll cut down the palm tree," he said.

"Not now, David. Mrs. Cooke would see you, and that would spoil the surprise. Wait until she goes out."

"I'll ask my aunt to invite her over this afternoon," Victoria said.

"Good," Lydia said. "Ask your aunt if we can pick some flowers from her garden. I'll get my shells." She ran up to her room and took a bag of seashells and some string from one of the drawers in her dresser.

When she returned to the courtyard, Victoria was back.

"My aunt is sending one of her servants with a note," Victoria said breathlessly.

Soon the servant came through the gate. He smiled and held up a piece of paper.

"That must be the note," Lydia whispered as he went inside. She and the other girls ran over to the kitchen window and listened.

"How nice of your mistress to invite me!" they heard Mrs. Cooke say. "I wish I could go, but I must finish making my Christmas pudding."

"Go tell her you'll make it," Lydia whispered to Bernice.

Bernice nodded and hurried into the house. The other children heard the door open as she entered the kitchen.

"Hello, Bernice," Mrs. Cooke said. "Victoria's aunt has invited me to come over this afternoon, but I must finish my pudding. Even if we don't have a Christmas tree, we must at least have a special pudding for Christmas."

"I'll finish the pudding for you," Bernice told her. "I'd be glad to."

"You, a royal princess, make a pudding!"

"I don't care about being a princess," Bernice said. "I'm eighteen. It's time I learned to cook. Besides, I watched you do it last year. Just tell me what to put in."

Lydia could tell Bernice was trying not to sound too eager.

"Well," Mrs. Cooke replied, "it would not be nice to refuse such a kind invitation. All right," she said to the servant. "Tell your mistress I will be there soon."

Lydia and Victoria covered their mouths so that Mrs. Cooke wouldn't hear them giggle.

They ran to the center of the courtyard and spread the seashells on the ground.

"Let's string them right now," Lydia said, picking out the prettiest ones.

"Quick, hide them!" David whispered. "Mrs. Cooke is coming."

The teacher came out of the door, straightening her bonnet. "I am going to visit your aunt, Victoria," she said. She looked at the shells. "What are you doing with the shells?"

"Just stringing them together," Lydia replied.

"Oh, that's nice." The teacher started toward the goat's yard.

"You'd better go the other way, Mrs. Cooke," Lydia said quickly. "You might get your dress dirty going through the bushes."

"I guess you're right." Mrs. Cooke turned around and walked toward the front gate.

"The longer she's gone, the better," Lydia whispered to the others.

David jumped up. "I'll cut down the palm tree," he said.

Lydia piled her shells into Victoria's lap. "I'll go get the flowers. Did your aunt say it was all right to take them from her garden?"

"Yes, but stay behind the trees so Mrs. Cooke won't see you," Victoria warned.

Lydia swung a basket over her arm. She ran through the goat's yard to the big garden on the other side of the shrubs. There were so many pretty flowers in the garden that she hardly knew which ones to pick first. A thick mass of pink blossoms grew on a tree.

"Those pink blossoms would look nice against the dark green palm leaves," she thought. She stretched her arms, but she could not quite touch the blossoms. She stepped up onto a rock.

Suddenly she heard footsteps. It was Mrs. Cooke hurrying along the stepping stones that led to the house. Mrs. Cooke was looking right and left, inhaling the fragrance of the flowers.

"If she sees me, she'll ask what I'm doing here," Lydia thought. "I'd better hide." Quickly, she stepped off the rock to duck under a shrub, but she lost her balance. Her basket dropped to the ground with a dull thud.

"She must have heard it," Lydia thought.

A voice called from the porch. "Good afternoon, Mrs. Cooke. I'm so glad you could come." It was Victoria's aunt.

144

"It was nice of you to ask me," Mrs. Cooke said. "I thought I heard something over by that tree."

"It was probably just a bird," Victoria's aunt said. "We have so many here. Do come in. I have made some tea."

Mrs. Cooke went inside.

"Victoria's aunt must have known it was I," Lydia thought. "She called out just in time." Quickly she added some white blossoms to her basket and ran back to the school.

David was hacking away at the palm tree in the courtyard.

"Faster! Faster!" Victoria urged.

Finally the tree fell to the ground. David put it in a bucket. He pressed some dirt around the trunk so that it would stand up straight. Then he carried the tree into the parlor.

He and Lydia fastened the brightly-colored flowers to the branches. Then Victoria trimmed the tree with strings of white shells.

The children stood back to admire their work.

"It looks beautiful!" Lydia cried. "If only we had a star! Mrs. Cooke told me that she always put a star on top of her Christmas tree at home."

"I have one!" David said. "I'll go get it."

Victoria and Lydia looked puzzled as he bounded up the stairs. In a few moments he was back, waving a dried starfish in the air.

The girls laughed.

"Well, it's better than no star at all," Lydia said. "Let's put it up."

"The pudding is done." Bernice came into the room wearing Mrs. Cooke's apron. "The tree looks lovely! Won't she be surprised? Now if it would only snow, she would have a Christmas just like the ones she remembers. Even you can't arrange for snow, Lydia."

Lydia looked down at her basket. There were a few white blossoms left. Her eyes twinkled.

"It will snow," she said mysteriously. "Sh, I

146

hear Mrs. Cooke at the door. Let's all sing 'Deck the Halls.'" She raised her hands and led the others in song.

"Deck the halls with boughs of holly,
Fa-la-la-la-la, la-la-la-la.
'Tis the season to be jolly——"

Mrs. Cooke looked from the tree to the children and then back to the tree again. Lydia took the white blossoms from the basket. With both hands, she flung them into the air.

"It's snowing!" Victoria cried. "Just like Christmas in New England!"

The teacher smiled. "You have shown the real spirit of Christmas, children," she said. She took off her glasses and dabbed at her eyes with her white handkerchief.

Then she looked out the window at the darkening sky. "The same star that shines through the pine trees of New England shines through the palm trees of Hawaii," she said softly.

Bernice Is a Bride

A TALL young man with fair hair came to the Royal School one day.

"Good afternoon," he said to Lydia when she opened the door. "I am Charles Bishop from the United States. I would like to see Mrs. Cooke. I have messages from some of her friends in the United States."

"She is in the parlor," Lydia answered politely. "I will show you." She started toward the parlor and the young man followed her.

Bernice was just coming down the stairs. She was almost nineteen now. She wore a long dress with a wide skirt. Her hair was fastened at the back of her neck. Lydia still thought she was the prettiest sister in all Hawaii.

"Bernice, this is Charles Bishop," she said. "He has come to see Mrs. Cooke."

The dimple in the older girl's cheek deepened. "How do you do, Mr. Bishop. Lydia, you can go outside and play. I will show Mr. Bishop the way to the parlor."

A few minutes later, Mrs. Cooke came out into the courtyard.

"Has Mr. Bishop left?" Lydia asked.

"No, he is still here," the teacher said.

Lydia peeked through the parlor window. Mr. Bishop was talking to Bernice. He stayed all afternoon. When he left, Lydia noticed how brightly her sister's eyes sparkled.

"Don't you think Mr. Bishop is the handsomest man you've ever seen?" she said to Lydia.

"He's too tall," Lydia teased. "What's he doing here in Hawaii, anyway?"

"He came to visit, and he likes it so much he is going to stay. He is very nice, and he must be smart, too! The King has given him an important position in the government." Bernice giggled. She spread her arms wide and whirled around the courtyard.

"Silly goose," Lydia thought.

During the next few months, Charles Bishop came to the school often. Each time he came, he and Bernice talked together for a long, long time. Lydia noticed that they always managed to sit next to each other at church.

One Sunday, Lydia and Bernice went home for a visit. Papa Paki and Mama Konia no longer lived in the grass house. They had built a modern wooden house not far from the school.

"Father," Bernice said as they all sat together in the fine new living room, "I—I have something to tell you." Her cheeks were flushed. She fumbled with the locket around her neck.

Papa Paki leaned over and pinched her cheek. "Yes, daughter?" Lydia noticed how his eyes shone, just as they did whenever he looked at Bernice's pretty face. "Do you need a new dress?"

"No." Bernice took a deep breath. "I—I want to get married!"

Papa Paki looked sad for a time. Then he smiled. "When did Prince Lot propose?"

Prince Lot was Victoria's brother. He and Bernice used to spend a great deal of time together. "Until Charles Bishop came," Lydia thought to herself.

"It is not Prince Lot I want to marry, Father," Lydia said.

"No? Prince Alexander, then. They are both fine young men of royal blood. Either of them would be a proper husband for a Hawaiian princess. Congrat——"

"It is not Prince Alexander, either, Father," Bernice interrupted. "It is Charles Bishop."

Papa Paki's eyebrows rose in surprise. "Charles Bishop? Oh, yes, the young man from the United States. We met him at church. Hmmm, have you talked with him about the fact that you might be a queen some day?"

"Yes, Father," Bernice said quietly, "and he and I agree. I do not want to be a queen. I just want to be Charles's wife."

Papa Paki jumped to his feet. "You are descended from the first King of Hawaii!" he cried. "I have raised you to be a queen!"

Lydia was frightened. She had never seen Papa Paki so angry. His eyes flashed.

"You must change your mind!" he shouted.

"I cannot," Bernice said. "I love Charles. I want to marry him."

Papa Paki sat down. He bowed his head. "Then I do not wish to see you again," he said.

"Papa Paki!" Lydia cried.

"You had both better go back to school now."

He leaned back in his chair and placed his hand over his eyes.

Bernice was silent as she and Lydia walked back to school. Lydia could tell that Bernice was close to tears.

"Bernice, don't you really want to be a queen?" she asked. "I'd love to be one!"

"It is too bad you were not born in my place," said Bernice. "I would rather marry Charles than be queen of the whole world! Perhaps you will understand some day."

Lydia was quiet for a moment. "I would want to marry the man I love, too," she said. "Still, I would really like to be a queen!"

During the next few months, Bernice and Papa Paki did not see each other. Whenever Lydia went to visit him, he refused even to talk about Bernice. Still, Lydia knew that he missed his daughter very much.

Mrs. Cooke made arrangements for Bernice

and Charles to be married in the parlor of the Royal Boarding School. Finally the day of the wedding came. Lydia was helping Bernice get dressed. How lovely she looked in the long white bridal gown that Mrs. Cooke had made!

"She isn't as happy as a bride ought to be," Lydia thought. "If only Papa Paki would come!"

"Why don't you send him a note, Bernice?" she suggested. "I'm sure he'd come."

"I—I would like to," Bernice said. Then her lips formed a straight line. "No! He said he did not want to see me again."

Bernice's locket lay on her dresser. Lydia picked it up and opened it. Inside there were two pictures. One was of Charles. The other was of Papa Paki!

"I shall wear it," Bernice said, holding out her hand for the locket.

"Oh, the clasp is loose!" Lydia said quickly. "Before I get dressed, I'll have someone fix it."

She slipped the locket into her pocket and left the room. She ran down the stairs and out of the school before anyone could see her. She hurried down the path to Papa Paki's house.

He was sitting on the porch alone. "Is your sister married yet?" he asked. Lydia noticed that his brown eyes were misty.

"No. The wedding is at two o'clock. Please come, Papa," she begged. "Bernice feels awful."

Papa Paki's lips formed a thin line, just as Bernice's had. "Then why doesn't she ask me?"

"Because you said you never wanted to see her again!" Lydia reached into her pocket for the locket. She opened it. "Look."

He looked down. "She—she still wears my picture, as well as that of Charles Bishop?" he whispered, almost to himself.

"Yes. She is going to wear it at the wedding."

"Go back to school and help her dress." Papa Paki's voice sounded choked.

156

"Will you come?"

"I shall think it over."

The parlor of the Royal School was decorated with fragrant flowers and shiny leaves. The bridal procession started down the stairway. Lydia was maid-of-honor, so she went down the stairs first. She wore a beautiful long dress with a full skirt.

As she entered the parlor, she looked around. She saw Victoria and her brothers, her own brother David, Mrs. Cooke, two of Charles Bishop's friends—and Papa Paki and Mama Konia! Papa and Mama were sitting on a bench near the window. Papa wore his high chief's cape of yellow feathers.

Lydia took her place beside Charles at the flower-covered altar. She turned around and watched Bernice come down the aisle, which was really a carpet of flowers. A thin white veil covered the bride's face, but Lydia could see that she was not smiling. She had not seen Papa Paki.

157

He stood up and crossed the room with long strides. Bernice's face lighted up with happiness when she saw him. Father and daughter walked down to the altar together.

When the minister had finished the ceremony, Papa Paki took off his feathered cape and placed it about the bride and groom's shoulders. "This was the custom of the Hawaiian chiefs of old," he said. "I hope you will be very happy."

Bernice threw her arms around her father. Charles shook his hand hard.

"Now," Lydia thought, "Bernice is as happy as a bride should be!"

The Island of Maui

THE NEXT summer Lydia went to Papa Paki's house on the island of Maui. As they sat on the porch one day, Papa Paki told her the legend of the island.

"This island," he said, "was named after a lad called Maui, who was supposed to have lived here. Maui, the story goes, looked like a boy, but he could do wonderful things that a god can do. He performed his greatest deed when he was only twelve years old."

"Just my age!" Lydia said. "What did Maui do, Papa Paki?"

"Well, one evening Maui was watching his

mother take her clothes off the line. 'They are still wet,' she said, holding up the dripping clothes. 'The sun never stays out long enough to dry them.'

"Young Maui wanted to help his mother. He thought and thought. Then he had an idea. He braided the strings of many coconut husks together to make a long rope. That night he twined the rope over his arm and climbed to the top of Haleakala, which means 'House of the Sun.' "

Papa Paki pointed to the purple mountain in the distance. "That's Haleakala there," he said.

"Maui climbed fast, for he had very long legs," he went on. "In fact, some people say that he was so tall as a man that he could step from one Hawaiian island to another without even getting his feet wet! There are seventy miles between each island, so he must have had long legs!

"Well, when Maui got to the top of the mountain, he waited for daybreak. That is when the

160

sun starts its journey across the sky. When the sun was straight over Maui's head, he hurled his rope high into the air. He caught hold of one of the sun's rays and tugged and tugged until he pulled the sun down to earth.

"'Let me go!' the sun cried. It was so angry that it was even redder than it is at sunset.

"'You move across the sky too fast,' said Maui. 'The day is so short, my mother's clothes do not

have time to dry. If you promise to go slower, I will let you go.'

" 'All right, I promise!' said the sun.

"So Maui set the sun free and watched it rise to the sky. The sun kept its promise. From that day to this, it takes about twelve hours to move across the sky."

"So all the clothes dry!" Lydia laughed.

"Yes, and the fruit ripens, and the fishermen have more time to fish," Papa Paki added.

"It's a good story, even if it isn't true," Lydia said, gazing out over the ocean. "Look! There's a big ship coming around the point."

"It has probably come to take cattle to one of the other islands," Papa Paki said. "There is no wharf here, so the cowboys must lead the cattle right into the water and out to the ship. Come, let us go down to the beach and watch."

They joined the crowd that had gathered along the shore. Cowboys wearing only pieces of cloth

162

about their thighs and waists rode up and down on horseback. Dozens of cattle mooed restlessly in a corral, a fenced-off place on the beach.

"Aloha, Chief Paki." A cowboy with a rope coiled over his arm rode toward them.

"Aloha, my friend Pua," Papa Paki answered.

"Ah, this must be Lydia, the brave young daughter you told me about." Pua took the flower lei from the brim of his straw hat, leaned over, and placed it around Lydia's neck. "Your father tells me you ride horseback well. Would you like to ride with me, Lydia?"

She turned to Papa Paki.

"Pua is a fine cowboy," he said. "His horse is strong and specially trained for swimming. You may ride with him if you wish."

"I'd love to!" She held out her hand, and Pua helped her to his saddle in front of him.

"Hang on tight!" Papa Paki called after them as they rode toward the corral.

163

Lydia clutched the saddle horn as another cowboy opened the gate and they rode inside. Pua swung his rope high over his head. The cattle ran this way and that, trying to escape the lasso, but Pua soon roped a big steer. Pua led the steer out of the corral, across the damp sand, and into the ocean.

Lydia held her breath and gripped the horse's body tightly between her knees. Salty spray drenched her, and she could feel the horse's legs paddling beneath her. The horse was swimming through the water.

Suddenly, the steer on the other end of Pua's rope jerked to one side. The wet rope slipped from Pua's hand.

Lydia felt the pressure of the cowboy's feet as he urged the horse after the steer. The end of the rope floated over the swelling waves. Now it was almost within Lydia's grasp. With one hand still holding the saddle horn tightly, she

164

reached into the water. At that moment the rope
moved beyond reach.

Pua placed his strong hands about Lydia's
waist. "You can get it," he told her. "Try again
and I will hold you."

Leaning way over, Lydia stretched her arm as
far as she could. The end of the rope touched
her fingertips. "I've got it!" she cried, pulling it
toward her.

"Hang on! There!" Pua took the rope from her and wound it around his wrist.

The steer stopped struggling, and Pua guided it close to the waiting ship.

"Who's your new cowboy?" one of the men on deck shouted as he swung a big sling over the side and lowered it into the water.

"Chief Paki's daughter, and she's doing a fine job," Pua answered. He led the steer into the sling. "Haul away!"

Lydia looked up. She could see the bottoms of the steer's hoofs as the men raised it up to the deck of the ship. Then Pua turned his horse around and headed toward shore.

Lydia was out of breath when she and Pua rode up onto the sand.

Pua set her down beside her father.

"You were right, Chief Paki," he said. "She's a brave girl. She can ride with me any time."

Papa Paki's dark eyes shone with pride.

An Important Task

LYDIA WAS a grown young lady now. She no longer attended the Royal Boarding School, but lived with her sister Bernice and Bernice's husband, Charles Bishop. Both Papa Paki and Mama Konia had died.

One afternoon, as Lydia and Bernice were sitting together in the living room, Bernice said, "Charles is bringing a guest home tonight. I think you will enjoy seeing him."

"Who is he?" Lydia asked. "Do I know him?"

"You will see," Bernice answered mysteriously.

At that moment Charles came up the flagstone walk with a tall, thin young man.

167

"He looks familiar," Lydia said, "but I can't place him."

When Charles and his friend entered the room, Charles started to introduce him. "Lydia, I'm sure you remember——"

The young man laughed. "Let's see whether she does remember," he said. His eyes twinkled.

"There is something familiar about your eyes," Lydia said. "What is—why, of course! You're Johnny Dominis! You went to the day school next to the Royal Boarding School!"

"Do you remember the day you tried to show me how to light a fire with two sticks?" Johnny asked with a smile.

Everyone laughed.

"How could I forget?" Lydia said. "Mrs. Cooke made me go to bed after supper for a whole week after that."

"John is now General Dominis," Charles said. "He is working for our government."

168

After that Lydia and General John Dominis saw each other often. Finally they became engaged. Two years later, in 1862, they were married. They went to live in the big white house that John's father had built. John's father had been an American sea captain. He had called the house Washington Place.

Lydia and John were very happy in Washington Place. Alexander was King now, and John became an important government official under him. Lydia loved to sing and play her guitar, and she spent much of her time making up songs to entertain her friends. Finally she became the leader of the choir in Honolulu's church.

One Sunday the King approached her as she was leaving the church.

"Lydia," he said, "I have heard many of the songs which you have composed. I think Hawaii should have its own national anthem. Do you think you could write one?"

Lydia flushed. "I am honored that you ask me, Your Majesty," she said. "I will certainly try."

"Thank you," the King said. "I expect important visitors from the United States to come to church next Sunday. I should like the song to be ready by then."

Only a week to compose music and words for such an important song! Lydia was dismayed, but she could not disappoint the King.

When she got home, she went right to work. She strummed a few notes on her guitar, trying to get an idea for a melody. Nothing sounded right. "This must be a beautiful song," she told herself, "a song that will fill people's hearts with love for Hawaii."

She worked all week. She tried dozens of combinations of notes and words. When Friday came, the song still was not written.

That night, she tossed and turned in her bed. All the things Kaikai and Papa Paki had taught her about Hawaiian history raced through her mind. She remembered how her ancestors had traveled thousands of miles over the open sea to reach the Hawaiian Islands. She remembered how the first King, Kamehameha, had united all eight islands into one kingdom.

Suddenly she sat up in bed. She took her guitar from the bedside table. She started to play. Notes flowed one after the other, seeming to come from somewhere deep inside her. Her lips formed words.

> "Almighty Father, lend us your ear,
> Hear a nation's prayer,
> We humbly bow down before your throne,
> And ask your loving care.
> Give us peace throughout our land
> O'er these sunny sea-bound isles,
> Guard our nation's life, O Lord,
> Upon our good King, smile."

She lighted the lamp and wrote the words and music down as quickly as she could. When she was finished, she turned out the lamp and returned to her bed.

The next day she taught the words and music to the choir at church. Her brother David sat in one of the empty pews and listened. When the choir had finished, Lydia asked him how he liked the song.

"Do you want me to be truthful, sister?"

"Of course."

"It is nice, but it is not exciting enough."

Lydia's heart sank. David knew a great deal about music. What if he were right? It was too late to write another song now. The King and his visitors would be at church tomorrow!

When she got home, Lydia sang the song again. She changed some notes here, some words there. She added another verse.

"Perhaps it is a little better now," she thought.

The members of the choir came to church early Sunday morning. Lydia showed them the changes she had made and gave them the words to the new verse. As she watched the people enter the church, her knees trembled.

The King and his visitors sat down in the royal pew. Everyone's eyes were focused on Lydia. The King nodded. Lydia turned around and faced the choir. She lifted her hands. The choir began to sing.

When the first verse was over, the church was unusually quiet. The pages of the music crackled as the choir turned to the last verse.

> "Bless, O Lord, our country's chiefs,
>   Give them wisdom so to live,
>   That our people may be strong,
>   And to you their glory give.
>   Give us peace throughout our land,
>   O'er these sunny sea-bound isles,
>   Guard our nation's life, O Lord,
>   Upon our good King, smile."

The members of the choir put down their music. Lydia turned around and bowed. Everyone was silent. "They did not like it," she thought, feeling the color mount to her cheeks.

The minister started to speak, but Lydia hardly heard what he said. People did not like her anthem! She had disgraced the King!

When the sermon was over, she left the church with the rest of the people. As she started down the steps, someone called, "Lydia, wait!" She turned. It was the King.

He rushed over to her and shook her hand. "Lydia, you have done our islands a great service!" he said. "Did you see how quiet people were when the choir finished singing? They were too moved to speak or applaud. What do you call the song?"

"I call it 'The Hawaiian People's Song,' Your Majesty," Lydia said.

" 'The Hawaiian People's Song' is now the national anthem of Hawaii!" the King announced.

Everyone crowded around to congratulate

Lydia. Bernice whispered in her ear, "When you were a little girl, you said one day that you would write a song for the King. Do you remember?"

Lydia nodded happily.

"The song is lovely now, sister," David said. "All it needed was those few changes and the extra verse."

All the Hawaiian people liked Lydia's song and were soon singing it. However, a few years later she wrote another melody that became much more famous. It was called "Aloha Oe."

One day Lydia and several friends were riding horseback down one of the hillsides behind Honolulu. It was sunset. They stopped to gaze at the lovely scene before them. The brilliant flowers, the palm trees, the gleaming sand, and the red sky reaching down to the sea moved them all.

"Our islands are so beautiful," Lydia murmured. "It is no wonder that people come from all over the world to see them."

176

As the horses moved slowly down the path, Lydia started to hum a tune. Then she began to fit words to the melody.

"Aloha oe, aloha oe,
   Thou charming one who dwells
     among the bowers,
   One fond embrace before I now depart,
   Until we meet again."

When she was finished, one of her friends sighed. "That was beautiful, Lydia. You should write it down so other people could hear it."

When she reached home, Lydia did write the melody down. Everyone told her to send it to a music publisher in San Francisco. The publisher accepted the song at once. Before long, people all over the world were singing "Aloha Oe." It has remained a favorite throughout the years.

Today, when visitors arrive and leave Hawaii, either by steamship or airplane, musicians are on hand to play "Aloha Oe." "Aloha" means "hello," "good-by," or "love." "Oe" means "to you." The musicians play "Aloha Oe" both as a greeting and as a farewell.

Lydia's song has become the musical symbol of the beauty and personality of the lovely islands far out in the Pacific Ocean.

Hawaii's Last Queen

Twelve years passed. All the descendents of the first King of Hawaii had died except Bernice, and she did not wish to be Queen. David, Lydia's brother, was elected King under the name Kalakaua. Lydia was really a princess at last!

One day, several years after David had become King, Lydia was working in her garden at Washington Place. A servant came hunting her.

"There was a message from the palace, Your Highness," he said. "The King wishes to see you as soon as possible."

"I wonder what he wants," Lydia thought as she hurried to the palace.

The guard at the door bowed and showed her into the throne room. It was a beautiful room with glittering chandeliers, great mirrors, and velvet hangings on the walls. However, the King was not there.

"He is probably in the boathouse behind the palace, Your Highness," the guard said.

Lydia smiled. David still loved the sea. She remembered the day he had taken her for her first ride on a surfboard.

When she entered the boathouse, she found the King in old clothes, painting one of his boats.

"Aloha, Lydia," he said. "I have important news for you. I am going on a long ocean voyage. I want to take the good wishes of the people of Hawaii to other nations."

"A fine idea!" Lydia said. "The nations of the world should get to know us better. Who will take care of things while you are gone?"

The King grew serious. "I hope you will."

This was the first time that Lydia had been called upon to take part in governing the country. She felt deeply honored, but a little frightened, too. However, she showed that she was wise, generous, and able to rule well.

A few weeks after the King had left, one of his advisers came to see Lydia.

"I am here on a serious matter, Your Highness," he said. "A number of cases of smallpox have been reported in the city."

Smallpox was a serious disease among the Hawaiians. Few people had been vaccinated to prevent it, and many of those who got it died.

Lydia said nothing for a few moments. She was remembering the time when measles visited the Royal Boarding School. She knew that smallpox was more dangerous than measles. Finally she said, "Make sure the sick are cared for. The hospital must open its doors to rich and poor alike. We must take care of the sick."

"Yes, Your Highness."

"Do everything you can to prevent the spread of the disease. See that the families of the sick do not leave their homes. I shall have food brought to them."

"I shall attend to it at once, Your Highness." The King's adviser started to leave.

"Wait! One thing more," Lydia said. "We must not let the illness spread to the other islands. Let the people know that no one is allowed to travel until the smallpox is gone."

"How can we do that, Your Highness? Many people earn a living by taking their goods to other islands, you know."

"I know, but the health of our people is more important. The goods may be sent, but no one from this island may go to another island until the illness has passed."

"I will see to it, Your Highness." The adviser bowed and left.

182

Because Princess Lydia made this decision, the illness did not spread to the other islands. When it was over, everyone praised her wisdom.

Lydia proved her love for her people in other ways also. A few months later she heard that a volcano had erupted on the big island of Hawaii. This time the eruption lasted for many weeks. It looked as if the crater might overflow.

She went to Hawaii by steamer and stayed there until she was sure that the people were safe.

When the King returned from his journey he was pleased with the way Lydia had handled matters. "You have done a fine job, Lydia," he said. "You may be sure that the people love you."

David Kalakaua was King for seventeen years. During those years Lydia helped him in many ways. Once she and John went with the Queen to England. The King wanted them to represent Hawaii at the celebration of Queen Victoria's fiftieth year as Queen of England.

On the way, the party visited the United States. In Washington, D.C., President Cleveland and his wife invited them to dine at the White House.

The Queen sat on the President's right at the table, and Lydia on his left.

"Mr. President," Lydia said, "we are deeply honored to have been invited here."

President Cleveland smiled. "It is we who are honored to have you, Your Highness," he said. "The American people have long admired Hawaii's amazing progress."

When Lydia returned home, a young Scottish poet was visiting the islands. He and Lydia became close friends. They spent many hours together making up songs and poems. His name was Robert Louis Stevenson.

In 1891 King David Kalakaua became ill and died. Princess Lydia was chosen to follow him as Queen Liliuokalani.

184

Lydia was saddened by David's death. Few members of her family and few of her old friends were left now. Bernice, Victoria, Alexander, Moses, Lot, David—they were all gone. Only John and a young niece remained.

Lydia took the oath of office in one of the council rooms at the palace. With John at her side, she placed her hand on the Bible. "I will always be loyal to the people of Hawaii," she said in a low voice.

Afterward, at home, John said, "Well, my dear, we never thought, years ago when we were children, that you would be a queen. Do you remember the day I asked you if you were a real princess?"

"Yes," Lydia said with a smile. "You climbed over the school wall." Then she added more seriously, "It makes me feel proud to have been named Queen, but it frightens me, too, John. I'm glad that I have you to advise me and help me do what is right. I don't know what I would do without you."

"I'll always be here," he said. "You may depend on that."

Unfortunately, Lydia found herself alone. Not long after she became Queen, John fell ill. Within a few months he had joined Bernice and David and all the other members of the royal family.

Her sorrow was great, but John's death was only the beginning of her troubles.

Times were changing in the Hawaiian Islands. The Hawaiian people themselves were slowly dying out. Meanwhile more and more people were coming to the islands from the United States. Many of these people did not like the Hawaiian government. They wanted Hawaii to become part of the United States. Lydia wanted it to remain an independent kingdom, governed by the Hawaiian people themselves.

In 1893 the Americans carried out a peaceful revolution. Lydia was removed from the throne. A new government was set up to rule the country until the United States voted to make Hawaii one of its territories.

After this, Lydia retired to Washington Place and took no further part in political affairs. She helped her people in every way she could. She gave away much of the land she owned so that her people could have homes of their own.

The Hawaiian people loved her dearly. They showed their love by naming things in her honor. Even today there are streets, schools, parks, churches, and buildings named after her.

One day in 1917 Liliuokalani was sitting at the piano in the living room of her home, playing one of her favorite melodies. While she was playing, a servant hurried into the room.

"Your Maj—Madam!" he cried excitedly.

Liliuokalani looked up from the piano.

"The United States is at war with Germany!" the servant went on. "Word has just been received from the States."

Liliuokalani looked thoughtful. "That means that many of our boys will be fighting with the American Army," she murmured. "Some of them may be wounded or killed."

"Yes, Madam."

Liliuokalani rose from the piano. "Bring me an American flag," she ordered.

With her head high, she walked outside. Then the last Queen of Hawaii raised the flag of the United States over her home. All her bitterness and sorrow were gone. She felt only pride in her young countrymen who were fighting to protect their world.

She looked up at the flag fluttering in the wind. The stars and stripes looked beautiful against the deep blue of the Hawaiian sky.

"Now, truly, it is our flag, too," she thought.

A New State

ON THE morning of March 12, 1959, a young girl named Mary Makalena sat at her desk in her classroom in Honolulu. Suddenly a voice over the loudspeaker said, "Attention! Hawaii has just become the fiftieth state in the Union!"

Mary jumped from her seat and joined her classmates and teacher in a long loud cheer. Hawaii had waited a long time for this day! Finally the class settled down.

"School will be dismissed early today," the teacher said. "There will be no school tomorrow. You will all want to join the celebration."

As soon as the teacher let the class go, Mary

ran outside. Church bells were ringing, fire-crackers were popping, and ships' whistles were tooting. They were spreading the news.

Mary joined the crowd that was swarming into one of the city's best-known churches. It was the very church in which Liliuokalani had first sung her national anthem for the King.

Inside, the minister began to talk about Hawaii. He told of the Hawaiians of long ago, who had come to the islands in their outrigger canoes. He talked about their songs, their dances, and their great kings and queens.

Then he told his listeners how the missionaries had come to the islands one hundred and thirty-nine years ago. He reminded them how rapidly the Hawaiian people had progressed under the missionaries and how the islands had become a prosperous and up-to-date country. Now, he pointed out, Hawaii was a full-fledged member of the United States.

Mary left the church as soon as the minister had finished speaking. On the way home, she stopped at Washington Place, the home in which Queen Liliuokalani had spent her last years. In front of the house was a bronze tablet. Mary stopped to read it.

"Aloha Oe," said the raised letters at the top of the tablet. Below were the Hawaiian words of Queen Liliuokalani's famous song.

Mary read them thoughtfully. Then she looked up at the broad veranda running around the house. Liliuokalani had loved this house, just as she had loved Hawaii.

"I'm sure she would be happy if she could know that Hawaii is now a state," Mary thought. She ran her fingers lightly over the letters on the bronze tablet.

"Aloha oe," she murmured. "Hello and farewell. Aloha oe, Queen of Hawaii!"